RELATIVISTIC HYDRODYNAMICS

AND

MAGNETOHYDRODYNAMICS

THE MATHEMATICAL PHYSICS MONOGRAPH SERIES

A. S. Wightman, Editor
Princeton University

Ralph Abraham (*Princeton University*)	FOUNDATIONS OF MECHANICS
Freeman J. Dyson (*The Institute for Advanced Study*)	SYMMETRY GROUPS IN NUCLEAR AND PARTICLE PHYSICS
Robert Hermann (*Argonne National Laboratory*)	LIE GROUPS FOR PHYSICISTS
Rudolph C. Hwa (*State University of New York at Stony Brook*) and Vigdor L. Teplitz (*Massachusetts Institute of Technology*)	HOMOLOGY AND FEYNMAN INTEGRALS
André Lichnerowicz (*Collège de France*)	RELATIVISTIC HYDRODYNAMICS AND MAGNETO-HYDRODYNAMICS
George W. Mackey (*Harvard University*)	THE MATHEMATICAL FOUNDATIONS OF QUANTUM MECHANICS
Roger G. Newton (*Indiana University*)	THE COMPLEX *j*-PLANE
R. F. Streater (*Imperial College of Science and Technology*) and A. S. Wightman (*Princeton University*)	PCT, SPIN AND STATISTICS, AND ALL THAT

RELATIVISTIC HYDRODYNAMICS AND MAGNETOHYDRODYNAMICS

Lectures on the Existence of Solutions

ANDRE LICHNEROWICZ
Collège de France

W. A. BENJAMIN, INC.
New York *Amsterdam* *1967*

RELATIVISTIC HYDRODYNAMICS AND MAGNETOHYDRODYNAMICS
Lectures on the Existence of Solutions

Library of Congress Catalog Card Number 67-18400
Manufactured in the United States of America

The manuscript was put into production on November 4, 1967;
this volume was published on June 30, 1967

W. A. BENJAMIN, INC.
New York, New York 10016

PREFACE

This book is the result of lectures given at the Southwest Center of Advanced Study, Dallas, Texas, during October and November 1965. The lectures were presented to a small group of graduate students, and are collected here in the hope that they may be of interest to a wider audience of workers in hydrodynamics.

We assume that the reader is familiar with elementary concepts from the theory of relativity and with general theorems in partial differential equations.

The general purpose of the book is the mathematical study of the equations of relativistic hydrodynamics. We know the present importance of hydrodynamics and magnetohydrodynamics in relativity, from the mathematical and the physical points of view. The fluid studied here is a thermodynamical perfect fluid, with a vanishing heat current, which corresponds to the assumptions of A. H. Taub [14]. We will give in detail the proofs of existence and uniqueness theorems for the Cauchy problem concerning the different cases studied.

In the first three parts, we assume that the reader knows the elements of relativistic hydrodynamics (cf. [7], [10], for example), and we discuss the case of a pure fluid and also that of a charged fluid with a null conductivity in an electromagnetic field. The main tool used here is Leray's theorem for strictly hyperbolic systems [5]. This theorem is analyzed in Chapter 1. In Chapters 2 and 3 we show by two different methods that it is possible to deduce from the system of field equations a Leray system. In one of the methods, the vorticity tensor occurs and the relativistic Helmholtz equations are deduced for both charged and uncharged fluids.

In Chapter 4 we analyze the more difficult case of relativistic magnetohydrodynamics (infinite conductivity) and we determine the corresponding characteristics, that is to say the different systems of waves (magnetohydrodynamical waves, Alfven waves). The main system of magnetohydrodynamics is hyperbolic, but not strictly hyperbolic, and a more powerful theorem of Leray and Ohya is necessary to obtain a weaker existence theorem.

Chapter 5 concerns the theory of shock waves in relativistic magnetohydrodynamics. One of the purposes of this chapter is to show the simplicity of the relativistic theory with respect to the classical theory. For example, a shock wave is here an Alfven wave after the shock if and only if it is an Alfven wave before the shock (Alfven shock). In the relativistic frame, there is interdiction of the classical phenomena, called creator or destructor shocks. The properties of the Alfven shocks lead us to a direct study of the compatibility of a shock wave with the Alfven waves, and thus to the definition and the properties of slow shocks and fast shocks.

We will give the relativistic form of the classical compressibility conditions for a fluid. From the relativistic extension of the Hugoniot equation and from the previous conditions, it is possible to study, elementarily and completely, the thermodynamics of the shocks.

I am grateful to the Southwest Center of Advanced Study for its pleasant hospitality, and to Professor Choquet-Bruhat and Professor Ivor Robinson for stimulating conversations.

ANDRE LICHNEROWICZ

Paris
March 1967

CONTENTS

Chapter 1

EINSTEIN EQUATIONS AND LERAY THEOREM

In this chapter we will introduce the basic mathematical tools which will be necessary for our study. We begin with the Einstein equations. Harmonic coordinates are then introduced, and these are found to lead to a particularly simple and straightforward formulation of the Cauchy problem. The theorems of Leray, which provide for the existence and uniqueness of solutions of the partial differential equations we shall encounter, are then introduced. Finally, as illustrations of the utility of these tools, we formulate the existence and uniqueness theorems for the Cauchy problem in the exterior (source free) case, and in the case of pure matter (pressure free dust).

1. Einstein Equations

(a) In each relativistic theory of the gravitational field, the main element is a differentiable manifold of dimension 4, the *space-time* V_4. We have, on V_4, a hyperbolic Riemannian metric, with signature + - - -, which can be written in local coordinates:

$$ds^2 = g_{\alpha\beta}\, dx^\alpha\, dx^\beta, \qquad \alpha, \beta = 0, 1, 2, 3. \tag{1-1}$$

The $g_{\alpha\beta}$ are the *gravitational potentials* with respect to the coordinates. In each point x of V_4, the inequality $ds^2 \geq 0$ defines the *elementary cone* C_x in x. Such a manifold V_4 admits global systems of time-like curves, but does not admit, generally, global systems of space-like hypersurfaces.

Our point of view is here *purely local.*

(**b**) Let $R_{\alpha\beta}$ be the Ricci tensor of the metric and let us consider the Einstein tensor:

$$S_{\alpha\beta} \equiv R_{\alpha\beta} - \tfrac{1}{2}g_{\alpha\beta}R, \tag{1-2}$$

which, according to the Bianchi identities, satisfies

$$\nabla_\alpha S^\alpha{}_\beta = 0, \tag{1-3}$$

where ∇ is the operator of covariant derivation.

In general relativity, the metric satisfies Einstein's equations:

$$S_{\alpha\beta} = \chi T_{\alpha\beta}, \qquad \chi = \text{const.}, \tag{1-4}$$

where the energy tensor $T_{\alpha\beta}$ is continuous by pieces. $T_{\alpha\beta}$ defines the sources of the field. In the domains where $T_{\alpha\beta} = 0$, we have the so-called *exterior case.*

2. Elementary Analysis of the Cauchy Problem

We will give, first, an elementary analysis of the Cauchy problem for the exterior case:

$$S_{\alpha\beta} = 0. \tag{2-1}$$

(**a**) Let Σ be a local hypersurface of V_4 which is not tangent to the elementary cones. If $x^0 = 0$ defines Σ locally, we have $g^{00} \neq 0$. The Einstein system is equivalent to the systems

$$R_{ij} \equiv -\tfrac{1}{2}g^{00}\,\partial_{00}g_{ij} + F_{ij} = 0,$$

$$i,j = 1,2,3; \quad \partial_\alpha = \frac{\partial}{\partial x^\alpha}, \ldots \tag{2-2}$$

and

$$S^0_\alpha \equiv G_\alpha = 0, \tag{2-3}$$

where the F_{ij} and G_α are functions, the values of which are known on Σ if we know the values of the potentials $g_{\alpha\beta}$ and the values of the first derivatives $\partial_0 g_{\alpha\beta}$ (Cauchy data). The system of Einstein equations has the involution property: if a metric satisfies the equations (2-2) and, over Σ only, the equations $S^0_\alpha = 0$, then it also satisfies these equations outside Σ. This is a trivial consequence of the conservation identities (1-3).

(b) We see that the system (2-2) gives the values on Σ of the six second derivatives $\partial_{00} g_{ij}$ which we call the significant derivatives for Σ. The four derivatives $\partial_{00} g_{\alpha 0}$ are absent.

It is possible to change the local coordinates, according to:

$$x^{\lambda'} = x^\lambda + \frac{(x^0)^3}{6} \{\varphi^{(\lambda)}(x^i) + \epsilon^{(\lambda)}(x^\alpha)\}, \qquad (2\text{-}4)$$

where $\epsilon^{(\lambda)} \to 0$ when $x^0 \to 0$. In this change, the numerical values of the coordinates of the points of Σ and the Cauchy data are invariant. The same is true, of course, for the $\partial_{00} g_{ij}$, but the new $\partial_{00} g_{\alpha 0}$ can have arbitrary values, according to the choice of the $\varphi^{(\lambda)}$. These four derivatives can be discontinuous through Σ. But, according to an axiom of the theory, these discontinuities have no physical meaning and vanish for convenient coordinates.

The significant derivatives can have discontinuities only if Σ is tangent to the elementary cones. The characteristics of Einstein equations, or *gravitational waves*, are defined by the hypersurfaces $f = 0$ tangent to the elementary cones:

$$\Delta_1 f \equiv g^{\alpha\beta} \partial_\alpha f \partial_\beta f = 0. \qquad (2\text{-}5)$$

The *gravitational rays* are the characteristics of (2-5), that is to say the null-geodesics of the metric.

3. Harmonic Coordinates

(a) In the following part, we use systematically *harmonic* coordinates or, more exactly, the left members of the conditions of harmonicity. It is clear that harmonic coordinates are a very precious instrument for the mathematical analysis of the system of Einstein equations, but have no special advantages for the physical interpretation.

Let us consider a scalar equation which admits the solutions of (2-5) as characteristics. The simplest equation which has this property can be written

$$\Delta f \equiv -\nabla^{\alpha} \nabla_{\alpha} f \equiv -g^{\alpha\beta} \nabla_{\alpha} \nabla_{\beta} f = 0, \qquad (3\text{-}1)$$

that is,

$$\Delta f \equiv -g^{\alpha\beta} (\partial_{\alpha\beta} f - \Gamma^{\rho}_{\alpha\beta} \partial_{\rho} f) = 0, \qquad (3\text{-}2)$$

where the $\Gamma^{\rho}_{\alpha\beta}$ are the coefficients of the Riemannian connection with respect to the local coordinates. It is clear that the characteristics of (3-2) are the hypersurfaces tangent to the elementary cones.

In the following part, d is the operator of exterior differentiation for forms (skew-symmetric covariant tensors), δ is the operator of codifferentiation for the tensors, that is to say the contracted covariant derivation, except the sign. With these notations, (3-1) can be written

$$\Delta f \equiv \delta d f = 0. \qquad (3\text{-}3)$$

This is the Laplace equation for the Riemannian manifold.

A system $\{x^{\rho}\}$ of local coordinates is called harmonic if the x^{ρ} are local solutions of the Laplace equation (3-1). We introduce thus the four quantities:

$$F^{\rho} = \Delta x^{\rho} = g^{\alpha\beta} \Gamma^{\rho}_{\alpha\beta} \qquad (3\text{-}4)$$

which depend on the potentials and their first derivatives.

(b) We associate with the F^ρ the quantities $L_{\alpha\beta}$ defined by:

$$2\,L_{\alpha\beta} = g_{\alpha\rho}\,\partial_\beta\,F^\rho + g_{\beta\rho}\,\partial_\alpha\,F^\rho. \qquad (3\text{-}5)$$

In the $L_{\alpha\beta}$ appear the second derivatives of the potentials. We have from (3-5)

$$2\,L_{\alpha\beta} \simeq \partial_\beta\,(g_{\alpha\rho}\,\Gamma^\rho_{\lambda\mu}\,g^{\lambda\mu}) + \partial_\alpha\,(g_{\beta\rho}\,\Gamma^\rho_{\lambda\mu}\,g^{\lambda\mu}),$$

where the symbol $\simeq$ signifies that we neglect terms depending on the potentials and their first derivatives. We thus obtain

$$2\,L_{\alpha\beta} \simeq g^{\lambda\mu}\,\{\partial_\beta\,[\lambda\mu,\alpha] + \partial_\alpha\,[\lambda\mu,\beta]\}$$

in which appear Christoffel symbols. It follows that

$$2\,L_{\alpha\beta} \simeq \tfrac{1}{2}\,g^{\lambda\mu}\,(\partial_{\beta\lambda}g_{\alpha\mu} + \partial_{\beta\mu}g_{\alpha\lambda} - \partial_{\alpha\beta}g_{\lambda\mu}$$

$$+ \partial_{\alpha\lambda}\,g_{\beta\mu} + \partial_{\alpha\mu}\,g_{\beta\lambda} - \partial_{\alpha\beta}\,g_{\lambda\mu}\},$$

that is,

$$2\,L_{\alpha\beta} \simeq g^{\lambda\mu}\,(\partial_{\alpha\mu}\,g_{\beta\lambda} + \partial_{\beta\lambda}\,g_{\alpha\mu} - \partial_{\alpha\beta}\,g_{\lambda\mu}). \qquad (3\text{-}6)$$

(c) The components $R_{\alpha\beta}$ of the Ricci tensor depend also on the potentials and their first and second derivatives. We will prove that $L_{\alpha\beta}$ occurs in a simple way in the terms of $R_{\alpha\beta}$ containing second derivatives. We have

$$R_{\alpha\beta} \simeq \partial_\lambda\,\Gamma^\lambda_{\alpha\beta} - \partial_\alpha\,\Gamma^\lambda_{\lambda\beta},$$

which can be written

$$R_{\alpha\beta} \simeq g^{\lambda\mu} \{\partial_\lambda [\alpha\beta,\mu] - \partial_\alpha [\lambda\beta,\mu]\} .$$

We thus obtain

$$R_{\alpha\beta} \simeq \tfrac{1}{2} g^{\lambda\mu} \{\partial_{\alpha\lambda} g_{\beta\mu} + \partial_{\beta\lambda} g_{\alpha\mu} - \partial_{\lambda\mu} g_{\alpha\beta}$$

$$- \partial_{\alpha\lambda} g_{\beta\mu} - \partial_{\alpha\beta} g_{\lambda\mu} + \partial_{\alpha\mu} g_{\beta\lambda}\},$$

that is,

$$R_{\alpha\beta} \simeq \tfrac{1}{2} g^{\lambda\mu} \{\partial_{\alpha\mu} g_{\beta\lambda} + \partial_{\beta\lambda} g_{\alpha\mu} - \partial_{\alpha\beta} g_{\lambda\mu}\}$$

$$- \tfrac{1}{2} g^{\lambda\mu} \partial_{\lambda\mu} g_{\alpha\beta} .$$

It follows, according to (3-6), that

$$R_{\alpha\beta} \simeq - \tfrac{1}{2} g^{\lambda\mu} \partial_{\lambda\mu} g_{\alpha\beta} + L_{\alpha\beta} .$$

We thus obtain the following theorem.

Theorem. In an arbitrary local coordinates system, each component of the Ricci tensor can be written

$$R_{\alpha\beta} = \overset{(h)}{R}_{\alpha\beta} + L_{\alpha\beta} \tag{3-7}$$

where

$$\overset{(h)}{R}_{\alpha\beta} = - \tfrac{1}{2} g^{\lambda\mu} \partial_{\lambda\mu} g_{\alpha\beta} + f_{\alpha\beta} (g_{\lambda\mu}, \partial_\rho g_{\lambda\mu}). \tag{3-8}$$

The $f_{\alpha\beta}$ are given regular functions, and the $L_{\alpha\beta}$ are defined by the formula (3-5).

4. Einstein Equations in Harmonic Coordinates

(**a**) Let us consider the general system of the Einstein equations

$$S_{\alpha\beta} = \chi T_{\alpha\beta}, \tag{4-1}$$

which can also be written

$$R_{\alpha\beta} = \chi (T_{\alpha\beta} - \tfrac{1}{2} g_{\alpha\beta} T). \tag{4-2}$$

It follows from the conservation identities (1-3) that the system (4-1) implies, for the energy tensor, the equations $\nabla_\alpha T^\alpha{}_\beta = 0$.

If a solution of Einstein equations is written in harmonic coordinates, we have $L_{\alpha\beta} = 0$ and this solution satisfies

$$S^{(h)}_{\alpha\beta} = \chi T_{\alpha\beta}, \tag{4-3}$$

where

$$S^{(h)}_{\alpha\beta} = R^{(h)}_{\alpha\beta} - \tfrac{1}{2} g_{\alpha\beta} R^{(h)}, \qquad R^{(h)} = g^{\lambda\mu} R^{(h)}_{\lambda\mu};$$

and also satisfies

$$\nabla_\alpha T^\alpha{}_\beta = 0. \tag{4-4}$$

Equation (4-3) can also be written

$$R^{(h)}_{\alpha\beta} = \chi (T_{\alpha\beta} - \tfrac{1}{2} g_{\alpha\beta} T).$$

(**b**) Conversely, let us consider a solution of the system (4-3), (4-4) corresponding to some Cauchy data on a spacelike *hypersurface* Σ admitting the local equation $x^0 = 0$, and such that

$$F^\rho = 0, \qquad \text{for } x^0 = 0 \tag{4-5}$$

and

$$S^0_\alpha = \chi T^0_\alpha, \qquad \text{for } x^0 = 0. \tag{4-6}$$

On the hypersurface Σ, we have

$$S^0_\alpha = S^{(h)0}_{\ \ \ \alpha} + (L^0_\alpha - \tfrac{1}{2} g^0_\alpha L), \qquad L = g^{\lambda\mu} L_{\lambda\mu}$$

and we deduce from (4-3) and (4-6),

$$L^0_\alpha - \tfrac{1}{2} g^0_\alpha L = \chi T^0_\alpha - \chi T^0_\alpha = 0. \tag{4-7}$$

But from (3-5) it follows that

$$2L^0_\alpha = g_{\alpha\rho} g^{0\beta} \partial_\beta F^\rho + \partial_\alpha F^0, \qquad L = \partial_\rho F^\rho;$$

that is, according to (4-5),

$$2L^0_\alpha = g_{\alpha\rho} g^{00} \partial_0 F^\rho + \partial_\alpha F^0, \qquad L = \partial_0 F^0.$$

Equation (4-7) gives thus on Σ :

$$g_{\alpha\rho} g^{00} \partial_0 F^\rho + (\partial_\alpha F^0 - g^0_\alpha \partial_0 F^0) = 0,$$

that is,

$$g_{\alpha\rho} g^{00} \partial_0 F^\rho = 0.$$

Since g^{00} is different from zero, we see that our solution of (4-3) and (4-4) satisfies on Σ:

$$\partial_0 F^\rho = 0, \qquad \text{for } x^0 = 0. \tag{4-8}$$

(c) For our solution of (4-3) and (4-4), we have

$$\nabla_\lambda (L^{\lambda\mu} - \tfrac{1}{2} g^{\lambda\mu} L) = \nabla_\lambda S^{\lambda\mu} - \nabla_\lambda S^{(h)\lambda\mu} = -\chi \nabla_\lambda T^{\lambda\mu}$$

and, according to (4-4),

$$\nabla_\lambda (L^{\lambda\mu} - \tfrac{1}{2} g^{\lambda\mu} L) = 0 . \tag{4-9}$$

But

$$2 L^{\lambda\mu} - g^{\lambda\mu} L = g^{\mu\rho} \partial_\rho F^\lambda + g^{\lambda\rho} \partial_\rho F^\mu - g^{\lambda\mu} \partial_\rho F^\rho$$

and

$$\partial_\lambda (2 L^{\lambda\mu} - g^{\lambda\mu} L)$$

$$= g^{\mu\rho} \partial_{\lambda\rho} F^\lambda + g^{\lambda\rho} \partial_{\lambda\rho} F^\mu - g^{\lambda\mu} \partial_{\lambda\rho} F^\rho + [O],$$

where $[O]$ denotes linear terms with respect to the $\partial_\rho F^\lambda$. It follows that (4-9) can be written

$$g^{\lambda\rho} \partial_{\lambda\rho} F^\mu + A^{\mu\alpha}_{\beta} \partial_\alpha F^\beta = 0, \tag{4-10}$$

where the $A^{\mu\alpha}_{\beta}$ are regular functions of the potentials and of their first derivatives. Thus the F^ρ satisfy the hyberbolic linear system (4-10) which admits a uniqueness theorem: If Σ is space-like, the only solution of (4-10) which satisfies $F^\rho = 0$ and $\partial_0 F^\rho = 0$ on Σ is the null solution. We have therefore $F^\rho = 0$ outside of Σ and so the coordinates are harmonic for our solution of (4-3), (4-4). It follows that this is the solution of the Einstein equations (4-1).

Theorem. Each solution of (4-3) and (4-4) satisfying $F^\rho = 0$ *and* $S^0_\alpha = \chi T^0_\alpha$ *on a space-like* Σ *is a solution of the corresponding Cauchy problem for Einstein equations.*

5. Strictly Hyperbolic Matrices

To prove existence and uniqueness theorems for the local Cauchy problem concerning our various differential systems, our main tool is an important theorem of Leray. We will give now the definitions and the statements which are necessary.

(**a**) Let V_n be a differentiable manifold of class C^k, where k is sufficiently large; $a(x, \partial)$ is a differential operator on functions, where $x \in V_n$ and where ∂ is the ordinary derivation

$$\partial = \{\partial_\alpha\}, \qquad \alpha = 1, \ldots, n.$$

Let T_x^* be the vector space of the covariant vectors at the point x of V_n. If m is the order of a, then $a(x, \xi)$ (where $\xi \in T_x^*$) is a real polynomial in ξ of degree m. We consider the main part $h(x, \xi)$ of $a(x, \xi)$, defined as the set of the homogeneous terms of degree m. Let $V_x(h)$ be the cone in T_x^* defined by the equation

$$h(x, \xi) = 0,$$

where x is fixed. We consider $V_x(h)$ as a projective conic surface. The operator a is called *strictly hyperbolic at* x if the following assumption is satisfied.

There exists in T_x^* *elements* ξ *such that each straight line issued from* ξ *and not containing the summit, cuts the surface of the cone* $V_x(h)$ *in* m *real and distinct points. Under these conditions, the set of these points* ξ *is the interior of two opposite convex half-cones* $\Gamma_x^+(a)$ *and* $\Gamma_x^-(a)$ *the boundaries of which belong to* $V_x(h)$.

(**b**) We consider now a diagonal matrix $A(x, \partial)$ sufficiently differentiable in x:

$$A(x, \partial) = \begin{pmatrix} a_1(x, \partial) & \cdots & 0 \\ \vdots & \ddots & \vdots \\ 0 & \cdots & a_p(x, \partial) \end{pmatrix}$$

The element $a_\tau(x, \partial)$ $(\tau = 1, \ldots, p)$ is a differential operator of order $m(\tau)$. The matrix $A(x, \partial)$ is called *strictly hyperbolic at* x if:

1. *The* a_τ *are strictly hyperbolic at* x.
2. *The two opposite convex half-cones*

$$\Gamma_x^+(A) = \bigcap_\tau \Gamma_x^+(a_\tau), \qquad \Gamma_x^-(A) = \bigcap_\tau \Gamma_x^-(a_\tau)$$

have a nonempty interior.

(c) We introduce, in the vector space T_x tangent to V_n at x, the convex half-cone $C_x^+(A)$, dual of $\Gamma_x^+(A)$. It is the set of the vectors **v** of T_x such that $\xi(\mathbf{v}) \geq 0$ for each $\xi \in \Gamma_x^+(A)$. With the same meaning, the opposite half-cone $C_x^-(A)$ is dual of $\Gamma_x^-(A)$ and we set $C_x(A) = C_x^+(A) \cup C_x^-(A)$. A path of V_n is called *time-like with respect to* A if the half-tangent in each point x belongs to $C_x^+(A)$. A regular hypersurface Σ of V_n is called *space-like with respect to* A if the vector subspace tangent to Σ at x is exterior to $C_x(A)$.

Let Ω be a domain (connected open set) of V_n. The matrix $A(x, \partial)$ is called *strictly hyperbolic in* Ω if the two following assumptions are satisfied:

1. $A(x, \partial)$ *is strictly hyperbolic at each point* x *of* Ω.
2. *The set of the time-like paths (with respect to* A) *joining in* Ω *two points* x, x' *of* Ω *is compact or empty.*

If $A(x, \partial)$ is strictly hyperbolic at x, it is possible to prove that there exists a domain Ω containing x, homeomorphic to the interior of a sphere such that A is strictly hyperbolic in Ω. In the following paragraph, we consider such a domain.

6. Leray Systems

(a) Let us consider, on the differentiable manifold V_n, the quasilinear differential systems with the unknowns

$$U(x) = (u_\sigma(x)), \qquad \sigma = 1, \ldots, p$$

which can be defined by

$$A(x, U, \partial)\, U = B(x, U), \tag{6-1}$$

where A is a diagonal matrix,

$$A(x, U, \partial) = \begin{pmatrix} a_1(x, U, \partial) \dots 0 \\ \vdots \quad \ddots \quad \vdots \\ 0 \quad \dots \quad a_p(x, U, \partial) \end{pmatrix}, \tag{6-2}$$

and where $B(x, U)$ can be written

$$B(x, U) = (b_\tau(x, U)), \qquad \tau = 1, \dots, p.$$

The elements $a_\tau(x, U, \partial)$ $(\tau = 1, \dots, p)$ of A are differential operators of respective order $m(\tau)$.

(b) In order to make precise the assumptions concerning $a_\tau(x, U, \partial)$ and $b_\tau(x, U)$, it is convenient to associate with each unknown U_σ *an integer index* $s(\sigma) \geq 1$ and with each equation τ of the system *an integer index* $t(\tau) \geq 1$ such that

$$m(\tau) = s(\tau) - t(\tau) + 1.$$

We assume that the b_τ and the coefficients of the differential operators a_τ are sufficiently regular functions of x, of the u_σ and *of the derivatives of* u_σ *of order* $\leq s(\sigma) - t(\tau)$. If $s(\sigma) - t(\tau) < 0$, the right members, b_τ, and the coefficients of a_τ are independent of u_σ.

The structure of the system (6-1) defines the indices $s(\sigma)$ and $t(\tau)$ up to an additive constant.

(c) We now define a Cauchy problem for the system (6-1). Let $\Sigma \subset \Omega$ be a local regular hypersurface of V_n. In the neighborhood of Σ we introduce

$$V(x) = (v_\sigma(x)), \qquad \sigma = 1, \dots, p,$$

where v_σ has locally square integrable derivatives of order $\leq s(\sigma) + 1$.

We assume that

1. *The matrix* $A(x, V, \partial)$ *is strictly hyperbolic in* Ω *and the hypersurface* Σ *is space-like with respect to this matrix* $A(x, V, \partial)$.

2. *The differences*

$$a_\tau(x, V, \partial)v_\tau - b_\tau(x, V)$$

and their derivatives of order $< t(\tau)$ *vanish on* Σ.

We consider, under these assumptions, the Cauchy problem defined, for the system (6-1), by the Cauchy data determined by V. A solution of this Cauchy problem *is a solution* $U = (u_\sigma)$ *of* (6-1) *having locally square integrable derivatives of order* $\leq s(\sigma)$ *and such that*

$$u_\sigma(x) - v_\sigma(x)$$

and their derivatives of order $< s(\sigma)$ *vanish on* Σ.

For this problem, Leray has proved existence and uniqueness theorems. More precisely we have the following theorem.

Theorem of Leray. If $x \in \Sigma$, *the Cauchy problem for the system* (6-1) *admits, under our assumptions, at least one solution in the neighborhood of* x. *If* $U = (u_\sigma)$ *and* $\bar{U} = (\bar{u}_\sigma)$ *are two solutions of the Cauchy problem in the neighborhood of* x *and if* u_σ *and* $\bar{u}_\sigma$ *have locally square integrable derivatives of order* $\leq s(\sigma) + 1$, *these two solutions coincide.*

(**d**) A system of the type (6-1) with the assumptions of section (b) regarding the nature of the coefficients of the a_τ and of the b_τ is called, in the following part, a *Leray system*. If it is possible to choose V such that $A(x, V, \partial)$ is strictly hyperbolic, we say that we have *a strictly hyperbolic Leray system*.

In the usual way, the Cauchy data are here the values on Σ of the u_σ and of their derivatives of order $\leq s(\sigma) - 1$, with some convenient compatibility conditions. The Leray theorem says that this Cauchy problem admits existence and uniqueness theorems, in the case of a strictly hyperbolic Leray system, if the Cauchy data are compatible and sufficiently regular.

7. The Exterior Case

We will give now relatively simple examples of the use of this theorem of Leray, which seems perhaps too abstract at this moment.

(**a**) Let us consider the Einstein system for the exterior case

$$R_{\alpha\beta} = 0. \tag{7-1}$$

In harmonic coordinates, we have

$$R^{(h)}_{\alpha\beta} \equiv -\tfrac{1}{2} g^{\lambda\mu} \partial_{\lambda\mu} g_{\alpha\beta} + f_{\alpha\beta}(g_{\lambda\mu}, \partial_\rho g_{\lambda\mu}) = 0; \tag{7-2}$$

that is,

$$g^{\lambda\mu} \partial_{\lambda\mu} g_{\alpha\beta} = 2f_{\alpha\beta}(g_{\lambda\mu}, \partial_\rho g_{\lambda\mu}). \tag{7-3}$$

It is easy to see that this system is a *Leray system*. The matrix A is here the 10×10 diagonal matrix whose diagonal elements are all equal and given by

$$g^{\lambda\mu} \partial_{\lambda\mu}. \tag{7-4}$$

(7-2) satisfies our differentiability assumptions, with the following indices:

$$s(g_{\alpha\beta}) = 2, \qquad t(R^{(h)}_{\alpha\beta}) = 1.$$

Indeed (7-4) has the order $2 - 1 + 1 = 2$. The coefficients of (7-4) and the right members depend only on the $g_{\lambda\mu}$ and on their derivatives of order $2 - 1 = 1$ at most.

(b) Let Σ be a local regular hypersurface defined by $x^0 = 0$. We consider Cauchy data such that:

1. *The quadratic form* $g_{\lambda\mu} v^\lambda v^\mu$ *is normal hyperbolic; the hypersurface* Σ *is space-like at each point with respect to the corresponding elementary cone.*

2. *We have on* Σ:

$$F^\rho = 0, \quad S^0_\alpha = 0, \quad \text{for } x^0 = 0.$$

If C^+_x is the future half-cone, its dual is the half-cone Γ^+_x defined by:

$$g^{\lambda\mu} \xi_\lambda \xi_\mu \geq 0, \tag{7-5}$$

with $\xi(\mathbf{v}) \geq 0$ if $\mathbf{v} \in C^+_x$. It is clear that we have *strict hyperbolicity*.

Therefore, if the previous Cauchy data are sufficiently regular, the theorem of Leray shows that the Cauchy problem corresponding to (7-2) admits one and only one solution. Mrs. Choquet-Bruhat, in 1950, proved this result directly.

The set of the time-like paths in Ω issued from a point y (or, ending on the point y) defines the future $\in^+(y)$ (or the past $\in^-(y)$) of the point y. If $\in(y) = \in^+(y) \cup \in^-(y)$ is the "emission" of y, the boundary of this emission is the characteristic conoid C_y corresponding to y, set of the null geodesics issued from this point. It follows from the theory of Leray that the values of the solution at a point y of the neighborhood of Σ, in the side of the future, depend only on the Cauchy data on $\in^-(y) \cap \Sigma$ (*the dependence domain*).

(c) $T_{\alpha\beta}$ being null, it follows from §4 that the previous solution of the system (7-2) satisfies everywhere the conditions of harmonicity $F^\rho = 0$ and thus is a solution of the system (7-1) of the Einstein equations. For Cauchy data satisfying $F^\rho = 0$ on Σ, we have thus obtained the existence of a solution of the Cauchy problem for Einstein equations in the exterior case.

The uniqueness of the Cauchy problem for the Einstein system is *a physical or geometrical uniqueness,* that is to say, the uniqueness, modulo a change of coordinates leaving invariant the numerical values of the coordinates of each point of Σ and the Cauchy data.

Let us consider a solution of the Cauchy problem concerning the Einstein equations $R_{\alpha\beta} = 0$ and corresponding to data with $F^\rho = 0$ on Σ. It is possible to construct a system of harmonic coordinates such that the coordinates of each point of Σ and the Cauchy data retain the same values. It is sufficient to consider the following system

$$\Delta f^\rho = 0, \quad \rho = 0, 1, 2, 3 \tag{7-6}$$

and the solution of (7-6) corresponding to the data on Σ

$$f^\rho = x^\rho, \quad \partial_\alpha f^\rho = \delta^\rho_\alpha, \quad \text{on } \Sigma .$$

The existence theorem for (7-6) implies the existence of such functions f^ρ, which define locally harmonic coordinates, and it is easy to see that, according to $F^\rho = 0$ on Σ, the Cauchy data of the initial problem retain the same values in the harmonic coordinates $\{f^\rho\}$.

We see thus that, if $F^\rho = 0$ on Σ, each solution of the Cauchy problem concerning $R_{\alpha\beta} = 0$ can be deduced from the unique solution of the same problem for $R^{(h)}_{\alpha\beta} = 0$ by a change of coordinates leaving invariant the numerical values of the coordinates of the points of Σ and the Cauchy data.

We have thus local existence and uniqueness theorems for the Cauchy problem concerning Einstein equations in the exterior case.

8. The Case of Pure Matter

(a) If we consider only pure matter as sources, we have the energy tensor

$$T_{\alpha\beta} = \rho u_\alpha u_\beta ,$$

where ρ is the proper density and u_α the unitary 4-velocity

$$g_{\alpha\beta} u^\alpha u^\beta = 1 .$$

Because of the unitary character of **u**, the conservation equations

$$\nabla_\alpha T^\alpha_\beta = 0$$

are equivalent to the system defined by the equation of continuity

$$\nabla_\alpha (\rho u^\alpha) = 0 ,$$

and the equations of motion

$$u^\alpha \nabla_\alpha u^\beta = 0 .$$

Our initial data, on a space-like hypersurface Σ, are defined by the values on Σ of the potentials $g_{\alpha\beta}$ and their first derivatives $\partial_0 g_{\alpha\beta}$. From these data, we can deduce the values of the S^0_α on Σ. From

$$S^0_\alpha = \chi \rho u^0 u_\alpha ,$$

it follows, according to the unitary character of u_α,

$$(\chi \rho u^0)^2 = g^{\alpha\beta} S^0_\alpha S^0_\beta .$$

It is necessary that the right-hand side should be strictly positive. We set

$$(\Omega^0)^2 \equiv g^{\alpha\beta} S^0_\alpha S^0_\beta$$

and thus

$$\chi\rho u^0 = \Omega^0 .$$

It follows that

$$u_\alpha = \frac{S^0_\alpha}{\Omega^0}, \quad u^0 = \frac{S^{00}}{\Omega^0}, \quad \chi\rho = \frac{(\Omega^0)^2}{S^{00}},$$

where S^{00} is assumed positive.

(b) Let us consider the system of Einstein equations for the case of the pure matter:

$$R_{\alpha\beta} = \chi\rho\,(u_\alpha u_\beta - \tfrac{1}{2} g_{\alpha\beta}); \tag{8-1}$$

with

$$g^{\alpha\beta} u_\alpha u_\beta = 1 . \tag{8-2}$$

According to the study of the harmonic coordinates (§4), we consider the system

$$R^{(h)}_{\alpha\beta} = \chi\rho(u_\alpha u_\beta - \tfrac{1}{2} g_{\alpha\beta}) \tag{8-3}$$

together with the system

$$\nabla_\alpha(\rho u^\alpha) \equiv u^\alpha \partial_\alpha \rho + \rho \nabla_\alpha u^\alpha = 0 \tag{8-4}$$

and

$$u^\alpha \nabla_\alpha u^\beta = 0 . \tag{8-5}$$

It is not possible for the system (8-3), (8-4), (8-5) to choose indices s and t such that the assumptions of Leray are satisfied. To obtain a strictly hyperbolic Leray system, we substitute for (8-3) the derivatives of these equations along the current lines, the trajectories of u^α, and then use (8-4) and (8-5). We have

$$u^\gamma \nabla_\gamma \{\rho(u_\alpha u_\beta - \tfrac{1}{2}g_{\alpha\beta})\} = u^\gamma \partial_\gamma \rho(u_\alpha u_\beta - \tfrac{1}{2}g_{\alpha\beta})$$

$$+ \rho u^\gamma \nabla_\gamma (u_\alpha u_\beta - \tfrac{1}{2}g_{\alpha\beta}).$$

It follows from (8-5) that the last term of the right-hand side is zero and so, according to (8-4), we have

$$u^\gamma \nabla_\gamma \{\rho(u_\alpha u_\beta - \tfrac{1}{2}g_{\alpha\beta})\} = -\rho \nabla_\gamma u^\gamma (u_\alpha u_\beta - \tfrac{1}{2}g_{\alpha\beta}).$$

We may now replace the 10 equations (8-3) by the 10 equations:

$$u^\gamma \nabla_\gamma R^{(h)}_{\alpha\beta} = -\chi\rho \nabla_\gamma u^\gamma (u_\alpha u_\beta - \tfrac{1}{2}g_{\alpha\beta}),$$

that is, by

$$-\tfrac{1}{2}u^\gamma g^{\lambda\mu} \partial_{\gamma\lambda\mu} g_{\alpha\beta} = -\chi\rho \nabla_\gamma u^\gamma (u_\alpha u_\beta - \tfrac{1}{2}g_{\alpha\beta})$$

$$+ u^\gamma f_{\alpha\beta\gamma}, \qquad (8\text{-}3')$$

where $f_{\alpha\beta\gamma}$ depends on the potentials and their first and second derivatives.

(**c**) We consider now u^α as an arbitrary vector. The unknown functions are the 10 $g_{\alpha\beta}$, the 4 u^α and ρ. We have thus 15 unknowns. The system (8-3′), (8-4), (8-5) is a system of 15 equations and it is a Leray system.

The matrix A, here 15 × 15, is a diagonal matrix, the diagonal elements of which are respectively[1]

$$a(3') = -\tfrac{1}{2}u^\gamma g^{\lambda\mu} \partial_{\gamma\lambda\mu}, \qquad a(4) = a(5) = u^\alpha \partial_\alpha. \qquad (8\text{-}6)$$

[1] The diagonal elements which are equal and which come from the same partial system are noted by the same symbol (a(3′) corresponds to the partial system (8-3′) ...).

This system satisfies our assumptions on the derivatives, with the following indices for the unknowns

$$s(g_{\alpha\beta}) = 3, \quad s(\rho) = 1, \quad s(u^{\alpha}) = 2,$$

and for the equations

$$t(3') = 1, \quad t(4) = 1, \quad t(5) = 2 .$$

Indeed a(3′) has the order $3 - 1 + 1 = 3$; $a(4) = a(5)$ has the order 1. Concerning the coefficients of the operators and the right members, we will give now a table where, for each unknown and for each equation, we indicate the maximum order of derivation which can appear, according to the indexes. Recall that if this order is negative, the corresponding unknown is absent in the corresponding equation. We have

$$(3')\begin{cases} g_{\alpha\beta} & :2 \\ \rho & :0 \\ u^{\alpha} & :1 \end{cases} \qquad (4)\begin{cases} g_{\alpha\beta} & :2 \\ \rho & :0 \\ u^{\alpha} & :1 \end{cases} \qquad (5)\begin{cases} g_{\alpha\beta} & :1 \\ \rho & :-1 \\ u^{\alpha} & :0 \end{cases}$$

These maxima order are compatible with the system (8-3′), (8-4), (8-5).

(**d**) Our initial data on Σ are, as we know, the $g_{\alpha\beta}$ and their first derivatives and we assume that these data are such that:

1. *The quadratic form* $g_{\lambda\mu} v^{\lambda} v^{\mu}$ *is normal hyperbolic; the hypersurface* Σ *is space-like at each point with respect to the corresponding elementary cone.*

2. *On* Σ *we have*

$$F^{\rho} = 0, \qquad \text{for } x^0 = 0 .$$

3. *The relations* $S^0_{\alpha} = \chi\rho u^0 u_{\alpha}$ *define a positive scalar*

ρ *and a unitary vector* u^α on Σ.

If C_x^+ is the elementary half-cone in the future, its dual is the half-cone Γ_x^+ in T_x^* defined by

$$g^{\lambda\mu}\xi_\lambda \xi_\mu \geq 0,$$

with $\xi(\mathbf{v}) \geq 0$ if $\mathbf{v} \in C_x^+$. To the operator $a(4) = a(5)$, there corresponds in T_x^* the "half-cone" $\hat{\Gamma}_x^+$ such that

$$u^\lambda \xi_\lambda \geq 0.$$

If u^λ is time-like for C_x^+, the intersection $\Gamma_x^+ \cap \hat{\Gamma}_x^+$ has a nonempty interior which is the interior of Γ_x^+. It is clear now that the matrix A is *strictly hyperbolic* and that $\Gamma_x^+(A) = \Gamma_x^+$. Time-like directions and space-like directions with respect to A are ordinary time-like directions and space-like directions.

From our initial data $g_{\alpha\beta}$, $\partial_0 g_{\alpha\beta}$, we deduce the values on Σ of the second derivatives of the potentials by means of

$$R_{\alpha\beta}^{(h)} = \chi\rho(u_\alpha u_\beta - \tfrac{1}{2}g_{\alpha\beta}).$$

Equation (8-5) gives the values on Σ of the first derivatives of the u^α and Eq. (8-4) gives the values on Σ of $\partial_\alpha \rho$. We know thus, for the system (8-3′), (8-4), (8-5), the values on Σ of the unknowns and of their derivatives of order $\leq s(\sigma) - 1$.

Therefore, we obtain for this system *which is a strictly hyperbolic Leray system,* a Cauchy problem. If the initial data are sufficiently regular, the Leray theorem shows that *this Cauchy problem has one and only one solution*($g_{\alpha\beta}$, ρ, u^α).

This solution satisfying (8-3′) and, *on* Σ, (8-3), therefore satisfies (8-3) everywhere. In addition, we have, according to (8-5),

$$u^\alpha u^\beta \nabla_\alpha u_\beta = \tfrac{1}{2} u^\alpha \partial_\alpha (u^\beta u_\beta) = 0$$

and therefore u^α, being unitary on Σ, is unitary everywhere.

From the argument of §4, it follows that our solution $(g_{\alpha\beta}, \rho, u_\alpha)$ is a solution of (8-3) and $\nabla_\alpha T^\alpha{}_\beta = 0$ and thus a solution of the Einstein equations (8-1), (8-2). We have thus proved *a local existence and uniqueness theorem for the Cauchy problem for the case of pure matter* (Mrs. Choquet-Bruhat).

Chapter 2

RELATIVISTIC HYDRODYNAMICS

In this chapter we will discuss perfect fluids: matter characterized by an isotropic pressure, a density, and an equation of state. We formulate first of all the relativistic thermodynamics of a perfect fluid. Our equations yield three types of characteristic surfaces: gravitational waves, stream lines, and hydrodynamical waves. We next prove the existence and uniqueness of solutions of the Cauchy problem for a perfect fluid. Finally, the special case of an incompressible fluid is defined, and studied in further detail.

9. Thermodynamical Perfect Fluid

(**a**) Let us consider a perfect fluid. The corresponding energy tensor is

$$T_{\alpha\beta} = \left(\rho + \frac{p}{c^2}\right) u_\alpha u_\beta - \frac{p}{c^2} g_{\alpha\beta}, \qquad (9\text{-}1)$$

where ρ is the proper energy density, u_α the unitary 4-velocity and p the pressure of the fluid. It is clear that

$$T^\alpha_\beta u^\beta = \rho u^\alpha .$$

Thus u^α is the time-like eigenvector of $T_{\alpha\beta}$ and ρ the corresponding eigenvalue.

In the following part, we adopt the point of view of Taub.

The proper energy density ρ includes a proper material density and an internal energy density of the fluid. We set

$$\rho = r\left(1 + \frac{\epsilon}{c^2}\right), \qquad r > 0, \tag{9-2}$$

where r is the *proper material density* of the fluid and ϵ its *specific internal energy*. This specific internal energy can be considered as a given function of two thermodynamical variables of the fluid, r and p for instance, the form of this function depending on the internal structure of the fluid,

$$\epsilon = \epsilon(r, p). \tag{9-3}$$

In (9-1) appears the scalar,

$$\rho + \frac{p}{c^2} = r\left(1 + \frac{\epsilon}{c^2}\right) + \frac{p}{c^2} = r\left(1 + \frac{\epsilon}{c^2} + \frac{p}{rc^2}\right).$$

We are led to introduce the scalar

$$i = \epsilon + \frac{p}{r} \tag{9-4}$$

which is called the *specific enthalpy* of the fluid. We thus have

$$\rho + \frac{p}{c^2} = r\left(1 + \frac{i}{c^2}\right) \tag{9-5}$$

and so the energy tensor can be written

$$T_{\alpha\beta} = r\left(1 + \frac{i}{c^2}\right)u_\alpha u_\beta - \frac{p}{c^2} g_{\alpha\beta}. \tag{9-6}$$

(b) The *proper temperature* T of this fluid and its *specific proper entropy* S can be defined, as in classical hydrodynamics, by the differential relation,

$$TdS = d\epsilon + pd\left(\frac{1}{r}\right), \tag{9-7}$$

where T^{-1} is an integrating factor for the differential form which is in the right member. From (9-4), it follows by differentiation that

$$di = d\epsilon + pd\left(\frac{1}{r}\right) + \frac{dp}{r}$$

and so we may write

$$TdS = di - \frac{dp}{r}. \tag{9-8}$$

The following treatment and the definition of the current vector differ slightly from those of Taub.

10. The System of the Stream Lines

(a) We know that Einstein equations imply

$$\nabla_\alpha T^\alpha_\beta = 0. \tag{10-1}$$

Explicitly, these equations of conservation for the energy tensor (9-6) of our fluid are

$$\nabla_\alpha T^\alpha_\beta \equiv \nabla_\alpha\left[r\left(1 + \frac{i}{c^2}\right)u^\alpha\right]u_\beta + r\left(1 + \frac{i}{c^2}\right)u^\alpha \nabla_\alpha u_\beta - \frac{\partial_\beta p}{c^2} = 0. \tag{10-2}$$

Multiplying by u^β, we obtain the *equation of continuity*

$$u^\beta \nabla_\alpha T^\alpha_\beta \equiv \nabla_\alpha\left[r\left(1 + \frac{i}{c^2}\right)u^\alpha\right] - \frac{u^\alpha \partial_\alpha p}{c^2} = 0. \tag{10-3}$$

According to (10-3), (10-2) can be written

$$r\left(1+\frac{i}{c^2}\right)u^\alpha \nabla_\alpha u^\beta = (g^{\alpha\beta} - u^\alpha u^\beta)\,\frac{\partial_\alpha p}{c^2}. \qquad (10\text{-}4)$$

So we obtain a differential system which defines the *stream lines* of the fluid, trajectories of the field of the 4-velocities.

(b) We assume, just for a moment, that the motion of the fluid is isentropic, that is to say, such that S = constant. From (9-8), it follows that

$$dp = r\,di,$$

and the system of the stream lines (10-4) can be written

$$\left(1+\frac{i}{c^2}\right)u^\alpha \nabla_\alpha u^\beta = (g^{\alpha\beta} - u^\alpha u^\beta)\,\frac{\partial_\alpha i}{c^2}.$$

If we introduce the positive scalar,

$$f = 1 + \frac{i}{c^2},$$

we have

$$u^\alpha \nabla_\alpha u^\beta = (g^{\alpha\beta} - u^\alpha u^\beta)\,\frac{\partial_\alpha f}{f}. \qquad (10\text{-}5)$$

The differential system (10-5) expresses the fact that, in the case of an isentropic fluid, the stream lines are *geodesics of the metric* $\overline{ds}^2 = f^2 ds^2$, conformal to the metric ds^2 of the space-time.

This result is a consequence of the following general lemma.

(c) *Lemma. If* f *is an arbitrary positive scalar and* u_α *a unitary vector field, set*

$$C_\alpha = f u_\alpha, \qquad \overline{g_{\alpha\beta}} = f^2 g_{\alpha\beta}.$$

We have then the formula:

$$\overline{C}^{\alpha} \overline{\nabla}_{\alpha} C_{\beta} = u^{\alpha} \nabla_{\alpha} u_{\beta} - (g^{\alpha}_{\beta} - u^{\alpha} u_{\beta}) \frac{\partial_{\alpha} f}{f},$$

where the $\overline{C}^{\alpha}$ *are the contravariant components corresponding to* C_{α} *in the metric* $\overline{g}_{\alpha\beta}$ *and where* $\overline{\nabla}_{\alpha}$ *is the operator of covariant derivation in this metric.*

We introduce the quantities

$$\overline{C}^{\alpha} = f^{-1} u^{\alpha}, \qquad C^{\alpha} = f u^{\alpha}.$$

From the expression for the Christoffel symbols, it follows that

$$\overline{\nabla}_{\alpha} C_{\beta} = \nabla_{\alpha} C_{\beta} - \frac{\partial_{\alpha} f}{f} C_{\beta} - \frac{\partial_{\beta} f}{f} C_{\alpha} + C^{\rho} \frac{\partial_{\rho} f}{f} g_{\alpha\beta},$$

that is

$$\overline{\nabla}_{\alpha} C_{\beta} = f \nabla_{\alpha} u_{\beta} + \partial_{\alpha} f u_{\beta} - \partial_{\alpha} f u_{\beta} - \partial_{\beta} f u_{\alpha} + u^{\rho} \partial_{\rho} f g_{\alpha\beta}.$$

Thus we obtain

$$\overline{C}^{\alpha} \overline{\nabla}_{\alpha} C_{\beta} = f^{-1} u^{\alpha} \overline{\nabla}_{\alpha} C_{\beta}$$

$$= u^{\alpha} \nabla_{\alpha} u_{\beta} - \frac{\partial_{\beta} f}{f} + u^{\alpha} u_{\beta} \frac{\partial_{\alpha} f}{f},$$

that is,

$$\overline{C}^{\alpha} \overline{\nabla}_{\beta} C_{\beta} = u^{\alpha} \nabla_{\alpha} u_{\beta} - (g^{\alpha}_{\beta} - u^{\alpha} u_{\beta}) \frac{\partial_{\alpha} f}{f}.$$

From this lemma results the interpretation of (10-5) given in section (b): the vector $\overline{C}^{\alpha}$ is unitary in the metric $\overline{ds}^2$ and we have $\overline{C}^{\alpha} \nabla_{\alpha} C_{\beta} = 0$.

(**d**) We come back to the general case and we introduce systematically the scalar,

$$f = 1 + \frac{i}{c^2}, \tag{10-6}$$

and the vector C defined by

$$C_\alpha = fu_\alpha, \qquad C^\alpha = fu^\alpha.$$

We call f the *index of the fluid;* it is a thermodynamical variable equivalent to the specific enthalpy; **C** is called, in the following part, the *current vector* of the fluid.

The differential system (10-4) can be written

$$fu^\alpha \nabla_\alpha u_\beta - (g^\alpha_\beta - u^\alpha u_\beta)\frac{\partial_\alpha p}{c^2 r} = 0.$$

But, according to (9-8),

$$\frac{dp}{c^2 r} = df - \frac{TdS}{c^2}. \tag{10-7}$$

Thus, for our differential system, we have

$$u^\alpha \nabla_\alpha u_\beta - (g^\alpha_\beta - u^\alpha u_\beta)\left(\frac{\partial_\alpha f}{f} - \frac{T\partial_\alpha S}{c^2 f}\right) = 0. \tag{10-8}$$

If we introduce the metric $\overline{ds}^2 = f^2 ds^2$, we deduce from the previous lemma that (10-8) can be written

$$\overline{C}^\alpha \overline{\nabla}_\alpha C_\beta + \left(g^\alpha_\beta - u^\alpha u_\beta\right)\frac{T}{c^2 f}\partial_\alpha S = 0 \tag{10-9}$$

or after multiplying by f^2

$$C^\alpha \overline{\nabla}_\alpha C_\beta + (g^\alpha_\beta - u^\alpha u_\beta)\frac{Tf}{c^2}\partial_\alpha S = 0. \tag{10-10}$$

11. Equation of Continuity and Conservation of the Matter

The equation of continuity (10-3) can be written

$$\nabla_\alpha (rfu^\alpha) - \frac{u^\alpha \partial_\alpha p}{c^2} = f\nabla_\alpha (ru^\alpha) + ru^\alpha \left(\partial_\alpha f - \frac{\partial_\alpha p}{c^2 r}\right) = 0.$$

According to (10-7), we obtain the following form for the equation of continuity,

$$f\nabla_\alpha (ru^\alpha) + \frac{rT}{c^2} u^\alpha \partial_\alpha S = 0. \qquad (11\text{-}1)$$

f, r, and T being positive, we see that, according to (11-1), the inequality

$$u^\alpha \partial_\alpha S \geq 0$$

implies the inequality

$$\nabla_\alpha (ru^\alpha) \leq 0.$$

These inequalities have clear physical meanings.

We say that the motion of the fluid is *locally adiabatic* if

$$u^\alpha \partial_\alpha S = 0, \qquad (11\text{-}2)$$

that is, if the specific entropy is constant along the stream lines of the fluid. According to (11-1), *saying that the motion if locally adiabatic is equivalent to the equation*

$$\nabla_\alpha (ru^\alpha) = 0, \qquad (11\text{-}3)$$

that is, to the remark that the proper material density r *is conserved. In the following part, we assume (11-2) or (11-3)* for otherwise the motion of the fluid is underdetermined. It is possible to consider that (11-3) is a necessary property of the material density.

12. Relativistic Helmholtz Equations

(a) The current **C** can be considered as a 1-form **C** and we associate to **C** its exterior differential

$$\Omega = d\mathbf{C}, \tag{12-1}$$

which is a closed 2-form ($d\Omega = 0$). This 2-form defines the skew-symmetric tensor,

$$\Omega_{\alpha\beta} = \partial_\alpha C_\beta - \partial_\beta C_\alpha, \tag{12-2}$$

which we have called the *vorticity tensor* of the fluid [7].

First, we shall give a form of the system of the stream lines which involves, in a simple way, the vorticity tensor Ω. According to $u^\alpha \partial_\alpha S = 0$, (10-9) can be written

$$\overline{C}^\alpha \overline{\nabla}_\alpha C_\beta + \frac{T}{c^2 f} \partial_\beta S = 0.$$

But

$$\overline{C}^\alpha \Omega_{\alpha\beta} = \overline{C}^\alpha (\overline{\nabla}_\alpha C_\beta - \overline{\nabla}_\beta C_\alpha) = \overline{C}^\alpha \overline{\nabla}_\alpha C_\beta,$$

since the current **C** is unitary in the metric ds^2. Thus for the system of the current lines, we obtain

$$\overline{C}^\alpha \Omega_{\alpha\beta} = -\frac{T}{c^2 f} \partial_\beta S.$$

On multiplying by f^2, we obtain

$$C^\alpha \Omega_{\alpha\beta} = -\frac{Tf}{c^2} \partial_\beta S. \tag{12-3}$$

If $i(\mathbf{C})$ is the operator of taking the inner product with **C**, we see that the system of the stream lines can be written in the form:

$$i(\mathbf{C})\Omega = -\frac{Tf}{c^2}\,dS. \tag{12-4}$$

This implies $i(\mathbf{C})dS = 0$, that is to say (11-2).

(**b**) Let $\mathcal{L}(\mathbf{C})$ be the operator of *infinitesimal transformation* (or Lie derivation) corresponding to the vector field **C**. It is well known that if Ω is an arbitrary form, then

$$\mathcal{L}(\mathbf{C})\Omega = [di(\mathbf{C}) + i(\mathbf{C})d]\Omega\,.$$

Here $d\Omega = 0$ and thus

$$\mathcal{L}(\mathbf{C})\Omega = di(\mathbf{C})\Omega.$$

By exterior differentiation of (12-4), we obtain the relativistic extension of the Helmholtz equations,

$$\mathcal{L}(\mathbf{C})\Omega = -\frac{1}{c^2}\,d(Tf)\wedge dS\,. \tag{12-5}$$

These equations can be written explicitly as

$$C^\rho\nabla_\rho\Omega_{\alpha\beta} + \nabla_\alpha C^\rho\Omega_{\rho\beta} + \nabla_\beta C^\rho\Omega_{\alpha\rho}$$

$$= -\frac{1}{c^2}\,[\partial_\alpha(Tf)\,\partial_\beta S - \partial_\beta(Tf)\,\partial_\alpha S\,]. \tag{12-6}$$

We shall see that these equations play an important part in the study of the system of the equations of relativistic hydrodynamics.

13. The System of Relativistic Hydrodynamics and its Characteristics

(**a**) In the following part, we adopt, as thermodynamical variables, the two variables f and S, that is to say the index of the fluid (equivalent to the specific enthalpy) and the specific entropy.

We assume then that r is a known function of f and S:

$$r = r(f, S).$$

The pressure $p = p(f, S)$ of the fluid satisfies then, according t (10-7), the differential relation,

$$dp = c^2 r df - rTdS. \tag{13-1}$$

(b) Now, we will study the Cauchy problem for the main system of relativistic hydrodynamics defined by the Einstein equations.

$$S_{\alpha\beta} = \chi T_{\alpha\beta} = \chi\left(rfu_\alpha u_\beta - \frac{p}{c^2} g_{\alpha\beta}\right), \tag{13-2}$$

with

$$g^{\alpha\beta} u_\alpha u_\beta = 1 \tag{13-3}$$

and by the equation

$$u^\alpha \partial_\alpha S = 0. \tag{13-4}$$

On the hypersurface Σ, with the local equation $x^0 = 0$, we give the values of the potentials $g_{\alpha\beta}$ and of their first derivatives, as well as the value of S. We assume that these data are such that $g_{\alpha\beta} v^\alpha v^\beta$ is normal hyperbolic, that Σ is not tangent to the elementary cones ($g^{00} \neq 0$) and that $F^\rho = 0$ on Σ.

We know that we can deduce from the data the values on Σ of the S^0_α. From

$$S^0_\alpha = \chi\left(rfu^0 u_\alpha - \frac{p}{c^2} g^0_\alpha\right),$$

and according to (13-3), it follows that

$$[\chi r f u^0]^2 = g^{\alpha\beta}\left(S^0_\alpha + \chi \frac{p}{c^2} g^0_\alpha\right)\left(S^0_\beta + \chi \frac{p}{c^2} g^0_\beta\right).$$

We set

$$[\Omega^0(p)]^2 = g^{\alpha\beta}\left(S^0_\alpha + \chi \frac{p}{c^2} g^0_\alpha\right)\left(S^0_\beta + \chi \frac{p}{c^2} g^0_\beta\right),$$

where the right-hand side is a function of the parameter p. The parameter p is assumed positive in the domain of p which we are considering. It follows that

$$u_\alpha = \frac{S^0_\alpha + \chi(p/c^2)g^0_\alpha}{\Omega^0(p)}, \qquad u^0 = \frac{S^{00} + \chi(p/c^2)g^{00}}{\Omega^0(p)},$$

$$\chi r f = \frac{[\Omega^0(p)]^2}{S^{00} + \chi(p/c^2)g^{00}}, \tag{13-5}$$

S being known on Σ; the last equation (13-5) is a condition on the possible values of f on Σ. This condition can be written

$$F(f; x^i) \equiv \chi r f\left(S^{00} + \chi \frac{p}{c^2} g^{00}\right) - g^{\alpha\beta}\left(S^0_\alpha + \chi \frac{p}{c^2} g^0_\alpha\right)\left(S^0_\beta + \chi \frac{p}{c^2} g^0_\beta\right) = 0,$$

where all the quantities depend on x^i $(i = 1, 2, 3)$, except p which is considered to be a function of f.

It is interesting to calculate the derivative F'_f. It follows from (13-1) that

$$\chi^{-1} F'_f = (f r'_f + r)\left(S^{00} + \chi \frac{p}{c^2} g^{00}\right) + \chi r f g^{00} r - 2g^{\alpha 0}\left(S^0_\alpha + \chi \frac{p}{c^2} g^0_\alpha\right) r.$$

Let

$$\chi^{-1} F'_f = (fr'_f - r)\left(S^{00} + \chi \frac{p}{c^2} g^{00}\right) + \chi rfg^{00} r.$$

But, from (13-5),

$$S^{00} + \chi \frac{p}{c^2} g^{00} = \chi rf(u^0)^2,$$

and so we have

$$F'_f = \chi^2 r^2 f \left[g^{00} - \left(1 - \frac{fr'_f}{r}\right)(u^0)^2\right].$$

Besides the data $g_{\alpha\beta}$, $\partial_0 g_{\alpha\beta}$, and S on Σ, we are also given the value of f on Σ, satisfying $F(f;x^i) = 0$, and such that $F'_f = 0$. The values on Σ of r, p, T and thus of the u_α are then known, and we have

$$g^{00} \neq 0, \qquad u^0 \neq 0, \qquad g^{00} - \left(1 - \frac{fr'_f}{r}\right)(u^0)^2 \neq 0.$$

(c) According to the argument of §4, we can substitute for the system (13-2), (13-3), (13-4) the system that includes (13-4), the 10 equations

$$R^{(h)}_{\alpha\beta} = \chi\left[rfu_\alpha u_\beta - \frac{1}{2}\left(rf - 2\frac{p}{c^2}\right)g_{\alpha\beta}\right]; \tag{13-6}$$

the equation, equivalent modulo (13-4) to the equation of continuity,

$$\nabla_\alpha(ru^\alpha) = r\nabla_\alpha u^\alpha + u^\alpha \partial_\alpha r = 0; \tag{13-7}$$

and the system of the stream lines which can be written, according to (10-8):

$$fu^\alpha \nabla_\alpha u^\beta - (g^{\alpha\beta} - u^\alpha u^\beta)\left(\partial_\alpha f - \frac{T\partial_\alpha S}{c^2}\right) = 0. \tag{13-8}$$

We note that, according to (13-8), $u^\alpha u^\beta \nabla_\alpha u_\beta = 0$ and therefore that u_β, which is initially unitary, remains unitary.

We will assume that the Cauchy data are given in terms of formal series in the local coordinates and we will seek formal series corresponding to these Cauchy data and solutions of the system (13-4), (13-6), (13-7), (13-8). We deduce from (13-6), since $g^{00} \neq 0$, the values on Σ of the derivatives $\partial_{00} g_{\alpha\beta}$. The equation (13-4) gives, for $u^0 \neq 0$, the value on Σ of $\partial_0 S$.

To obtain the values on Σ of $\partial_0 u^0$ and $\partial_0 f$, we note that (13-7) can be written

$$r\partial_0 u^0 + u^0 r'_f \partial_0 f = \varphi, \tag{13-9}$$

where the value of the right member φ is known on Σ. Likewise, the equation (13-8), corresponding to $\beta = 0$, can be written

$$fu^0 \partial_0 u^0 - [g^{00} - (u^0)^2]\partial_0 f = \psi, \tag{13-10}$$

where the value of ψ is still known on Σ. The equations (13-9) and (13-10) determine the values on Σ of $\partial_0 u^0$ and $\partial_0 f$, if the determinant

$$r[g^{00} - (u^0)^2] + fr'_f (u^0)^2$$

is different from zero, that is if

$$g^{00} - \left(1 - \frac{fr'_f}{r}\right)(u^0)^2 \neq 0. \tag{13-11}$$

If such is the case, $\partial_0 f$, $\partial_0 u^0$ and also the $\partial_0 u^i$ (i = 1, 2, 3), according to the equations (13-8) for $\beta = i$, have known values on Σ.

Under our assumptions

$$g^{00} \neq 0, \qquad u^0 \neq 0, \qquad g^{00} - \left(1 - \frac{fr'_f}{r}\right)(u^0)^2 \neq 0,$$

the same conclusions are available for the determination of the consecutive derivatives; it is sufficient therefore to derive in x^0 the different considered equations.

Thus, under these assumptions, the formal series that we sought are determined in a unique way. If the data are analytic, it follows from the classical argument of Cauchy-Kowalevska that we obtain one and only one analytic solution of the Cauchy problem corresponding to the system (13-4), (13-6), (13-7), (13-8).

(d) We have thus determined the characteristic manifolds of the previous system, that is to say the characteristics of the system (13-2), (13-3), (13-4). If $\varphi = 0$ is the local equation of a regular hypersurface, we obtain three types of characteristic hypersurfaces.

1. The *gravitational waves*, solutions of

$$g^{\alpha\beta} \partial_\alpha \varphi \partial_\beta \varphi = 0. \tag{13-12}$$

2. The hypersurfaces generated by the *stream lines*, solutions of:

$$u^\alpha \partial_\alpha \varphi = 0. \tag{13-13}$$

Clearly, these hypersurfaces are time-like.

3. The *hydrodynamical waves*, solutions of

$$\left[g^{\alpha\beta} - \left(1 - \frac{fr'_f}{r}\right) u^\alpha u^\beta\right] \partial_\alpha \varphi \partial_\beta \varphi = 0. \tag{13-14}$$

It is well known (see for instance Lichnerowicz [7], pp. 42-43) that the velocity v of waves with respect to the time-direction defined by **u** is given by the formula:

$$\frac{v^2}{c^2} = -\frac{u^\alpha u^\beta \partial_\alpha \varphi \partial_\beta \varphi}{(g^{\alpha\beta} - u^\alpha u^\beta) \partial_\alpha \varphi \partial_\beta \varphi}. \tag{13-15}$$

For the hydrodynamical waves, we have

$$-(g^{\alpha\beta} - u^\alpha u^\beta) \partial_\alpha \varphi \partial_\beta \varphi = \frac{fr'_f}{r} u^\alpha u^\beta \partial_\alpha \varphi \partial_\beta \varphi,$$

and (13-15) gives for the velocity of these waves

$$\frac{v^2}{c^2} = \frac{1}{\gamma}, \qquad \gamma = \frac{fr'_f}{r}. \tag{13-16}$$

In the following part, we assume that, in the considered domain, $r(f, S)$ is such that

$$\gamma = \frac{fr'_f}{r} \geq 1, \tag{13-17}$$

that is, $v^2 \leq c^2$. This is equivalent to saying that the hydrodynamical waves are time-like.

14. Laplacian of the Current C

Our purpose is to deduce from the system (13-2), (13-3), (13-4), a convenient system which is a Leray system. For this purpose, we will complete the relativistic Helmholtz equations by relations involving the Laplacian $\Delta\mathbf{C}$ of the current. These relations are consequences of the equation of continuity and of the equations of the stream lines.

(**a**) We consider the Laplacian of the current, which is canonically defined by

$$\Delta\mathbf{C} = (d\delta + \delta d)\mathbf{C}, \tag{14-1}$$

where d is the operator of exterior differentiation and δ the operator of codifferentiation. According to the definition of the vorticity tensor Ω, we have

$$\Delta\mathbf{C} = d\delta\mathbf{C} + \delta\Omega.$$

We are thus led to compute

$$\delta\mathbf{C} = -\nabla_\alpha C^\alpha = -\nabla_\alpha (fu^\alpha).$$

According to the equation of continuity $\nabla_\alpha (ru^\alpha) = 0$, we have

$$\nabla_\alpha u^\alpha = -u^\alpha \frac{\partial_\alpha r}{r}.$$

Thus

$$\nabla_\alpha (fu^\alpha) = u^\alpha \partial_\alpha f + f\nabla_\alpha u^\alpha$$
$$= u^\alpha \partial_\alpha f - fu^\alpha \frac{\partial_\alpha r}{r}.$$

This may be rewritten

$$-\nabla_\alpha (fu^\alpha) = fu^\alpha\left(\frac{\partial_\alpha r}{r} - \frac{\partial_\alpha f}{f}\right),$$

that is,

$$\delta \mathbf{C} = C^\alpha\left(\frac{\partial_\alpha r}{r} - \frac{\partial_\alpha f}{f}\right).$$

We introduce the function of the two variables $h = f^2$, and S, defined by

$$H(h, S) = \log (r/f). \tag{14-2}$$

It follows that

$$\delta \mathbf{C} = i(\mathbf{C})\, dH$$

and thus

$$d\delta \mathbf{C} = di(\mathbf{C})\, dH = \mathcal{L}(\mathbf{C})\, dH.$$

We obtain, therefore, for (14-1)

$$\Delta \mathbf{C} = \mathcal{L}(\mathbf{C})\, dH + \delta\Omega. \tag{14-3}$$

(**b**) We now try to compute $\mathcal{L}(\mathbf{C})\, dH$. We have

$$\partial_\lambda H = H'_h \partial_\lambda f^2 + H'_S \partial_\lambda S.$$

But

$$\partial_\lambda f^2 = \nabla_\lambda (C^\alpha C_\alpha) = 2C^\alpha \nabla_\lambda C_\alpha,$$

and therefore,

$$\partial_\lambda H = 2H'_h C^\alpha \nabla_\lambda C_\alpha + H'_S \partial_\lambda S.$$

And, if we introduce the vorticity tensor, this becomes

$$\partial_\lambda H = 2H'_h C^\alpha \nabla_\alpha C_\lambda - 2H'_h C^\alpha \Omega_{\alpha\lambda} + H'_S \partial_\lambda S.$$

But, according to (12-3),

$$C^\alpha \Omega_{\alpha\lambda} = -\frac{Tf}{c^2} \partial_\lambda S,$$

and so we obtain

$$\partial_\lambda H = 2H'_h C^\alpha \nabla_\alpha C_\lambda + \left(2H'_h \frac{Tf}{c^2} + H'_S\right) \partial_\lambda S. \qquad (14\text{-}4)$$

In this paragraph and in the following paragraph, we consider f or h as a function of the variables $g_{\alpha\beta}$ and C^α since $h = f^2 = g_{\alpha\beta} C^\alpha C^\beta$. From (14-4), we deduce

$$[\mathcal{L}(\mathbf{C})\, dH]_\lambda = 2H'_h C^\alpha C^\beta \nabla_\alpha \nabla_\beta C_\lambda$$

$$+ \left(2H'_h \frac{Tf}{c^2} + H'_S\right) C^\beta \nabla_\beta \nabla_\lambda S$$

$$+ \varphi_\lambda (1 \text{ in } g_{\alpha\beta},\ 1 \text{ in } S,\ 1 \text{ in } C^\alpha),$$

where the notation shows the maximum order of the derivatives which appear in the functions φ_λ. But

$$C^\beta \nabla_\beta \nabla_\lambda S = C^\beta \nabla_\lambda \nabla_\beta S$$
$$= \nabla_\lambda (C^\beta \nabla_\beta S) - \nabla_\lambda C^\beta \partial_\beta S.$$

According to (13-4), it follows that

$$[\mathcal{L}(\mathbf{C})\, dH]_\lambda = 2H'_h C^\alpha C^\beta \nabla_\alpha \nabla_\beta C_\lambda$$
$$+ \psi_\lambda (1 \text{ in } g_{\alpha\beta}, 1 \text{ in } S, 1 \text{ in } C^\alpha). \quad (14\text{-}5)$$

(c) It follows from a classical formula of the Riemannian geometry that we have

$$[\Delta \mathbf{C}]_\lambda = -g^{\alpha\beta} \nabla_\alpha \nabla_\beta C_\lambda + R_\lambda{}^\rho C_\rho . \quad (14\text{-}6)$$

From (14-3), (14-5), (14-6), we deduce that the current $\mathbf{C}$ satisfies the following system of equations:

$$[g_{\alpha\beta} + 2H'_h C^\alpha C^\beta] \nabla_\alpha \nabla_\beta C_\lambda - R_{\lambda\rho} C^\rho + (\delta\Omega)_\lambda$$
$$+ \psi_\lambda (1 \text{ in } g_{\alpha\beta}, 1 \text{ in } S, 1 \text{ in } C^\alpha) = 0. \quad (14\text{-}7)$$

Let us compute H'_h. We have

$$2H'_h = \frac{1}{f} \frac{\partial}{\partial f} \log \frac{r(f, S)}{f}.$$

But

$$\frac{\partial}{\partial f} \log \frac{r(f, S)}{f} = \frac{r'_f}{r} - \frac{1}{f},$$

and thus

$$2H'_h = -\frac{1}{f^2}\left(1 - \frac{f r'_f}{r}\right).$$

Using this expression, (14-7) can be written

$$\left[g^{\alpha\beta} - \left(1 - \frac{fr'_f}{r}\right)\frac{C^\alpha C^\beta}{f^2}\right]\nabla_\alpha \nabla_\beta C_\lambda - R_{\lambda\rho} C^\rho + (\delta\Omega)_\lambda$$

$$+ \psi_\lambda (1 \text{ in } g_{\alpha\beta},\ 1 \text{ in S},\ 1 \text{ in } C^\alpha) = 0. \qquad (14\text{-}8)$$

(**d**) If we apply to (14-8) the operator $C^\rho \nabla_\rho$, we see the term

$$C^\rho \nabla_\rho (\delta\Omega)_\lambda = -C^\rho \nabla_\rho \nabla_\alpha \Omega^\alpha{}_\lambda$$

and it is possible to compute this term by means of the Helmholtz equations. According to the Ricci identity, we have

$$C^\rho \nabla_\rho \nabla_\alpha \Omega^\alpha_\lambda - C^\rho \nabla_\alpha \nabla_\rho \Omega^\alpha_\lambda$$

$$= C^\rho [R^\alpha_{\sigma,\rho\alpha} \Omega^\sigma_\lambda - R^\sigma_{\lambda,\rho\alpha} \Omega^\alpha_\sigma].$$

It follows that

$$C^\rho \nabla_\rho (\delta\Omega)_\lambda = -C^\rho \nabla_\alpha \nabla_\rho \Omega^\alpha_\lambda + R_{\rho\sigma} C^\rho \Omega^\sigma_\lambda$$

$$+ R_\lambda{}^\alpha{}_{,\rho}{}^\beta C^\rho \Omega_{\alpha\beta}. \qquad (14\text{-}9)$$

But

$$C^\rho \nabla_\alpha \nabla_\rho \Omega^\alpha_\lambda = \nabla_\alpha (C^\rho \nabla_\rho \Omega^\alpha_\lambda) - \nabla_\alpha C^\rho \nabla_\rho \Omega^\alpha_\lambda$$

and so, according to the Helmholtz equations, we obtain

$$C^\rho \nabla_\rho (\delta\Omega)_\lambda = \chi_\lambda (2 \text{ in } g_{\alpha\beta},\ 2 \text{ in S},\ 1 \text{ in } \Omega_{\alpha\beta},\ 2 \text{ in } C^\alpha).$$

From (14-8) by derivation along the stream lines, we deduce

$$C^\rho \left[g^{\alpha\beta} - \left(1 - \frac{fr'_f}{2}\right)\frac{C^\alpha C^\beta}{f^2}\right]\partial_{\rho\alpha\beta} C^\lambda$$

$$= \alpha^\lambda (3 \text{ in } g_{\alpha\beta},\ 2 \text{ in S},\ 1 \text{ in } \Omega_{\alpha\beta},\ 2 \text{ in } C^\alpha). \ (14\text{-}10)$$

15. Existence and Uniqueness Theorem

(a) We take as unknown functions the 10 $g_{\alpha\beta}$, the scalar S, the 6 $\Omega_{\alpha\beta}$ and the $4C^{\alpha}$. We consider the partial differential system defined by:

(i) the 10 equations

$$R^{(h)}_{\alpha\beta} = \chi\left[r\,\frac{C_\alpha C_\beta}{f} - \frac{1}{2}\left(rf - 2\,\frac{p}{c^2}\right)g_{\alpha\beta}\right] \qquad (15\text{-}1)$$

(where f is considered as a function of the $g_{\alpha\beta}$ and of the C^{α});

(ii) the equation corresponding to the entropy

$$C^{\alpha}\,\partial_{\alpha}\,S = 0; \qquad (15\text{-}2)$$

(iii) the 6 Helmholtz equations which can be written

$$C^{\rho}\,\partial_{\rho}\,\Omega_{\alpha\beta} = \varphi_{\alpha\beta}\,(1 \text{ in } g_{\alpha\beta},\ 1 \text{ in S},\ 0 \text{ in } \Omega_{\alpha\beta},\ 1 \text{ in } C^{\alpha}); \qquad (15\text{-}3)$$

(iv) the equations (14-10) corresponding to the current

$$C^{\rho}\left[g^{\alpha\beta} - \left(1 - \frac{fr'_f}{r}\right)\frac{C^{\alpha}C^{\beta}}{f^2}\right]\partial_{\rho\alpha\beta}\,C^{\lambda}$$

$$= \alpha^{\lambda}\,(3 \text{ in } g_{\alpha\beta},\ 2 \text{ in S},\ 1 \text{ in } \Omega_{\alpha\beta},\ 2 \text{ in } C^{\alpha}). \qquad (15\text{-}4)$$

The system (15-1), (15-2), (15-3), (15-4) is a Leray system. The matrix A, here 21×21, is the diagonal matrix defined by[1]

$$a(1) = -\tfrac{1}{2}g^{\lambda\mu}\,\partial_{\lambda\mu},$$

$$a(2) = a(3) = C^{\alpha}\,\partial_{\alpha}, \qquad (15\text{-}5)$$

$$a(4) = C^{\rho}\left[g^{\alpha\beta} - \left(1 - \frac{fr'_f}{r}\right)\frac{C^{\alpha}C^{\beta}}{f^2}\right]\partial_{\rho\alpha\beta}.$$

[1]The notation is similar to the notation of §8.

This system satisfies our assumptions on the derivatives with the following indices for the unknowns:

$$s(g_{\alpha\beta}) = 4, \quad s(S) = 3, \quad s(\Omega_{\alpha\beta}) = 2, \quad s(C^{\alpha}) = 3,$$

and with the following indices for the equations of the system:

$$t(1) = 3, \quad t(2) = 3, \quad t(3) = 2, \quad t(4) = 1.$$

Indeed, we see that a(1) has the order 2, a(2) and a(3) have the order 1, and a(4) has the order 3. Concerning the coefficients of the operators and the right members, we will give the table where, for each unknown and each equation, we indicate the maximum order of derivation which can appear, according to the indices. We have

$$(1)(2)\begin{cases} g_{\alpha\beta}: & 1 \\ S\ : & 0 \\ \Omega_{\alpha\beta}: & -1 \\ C^{\alpha}\ : & 0 \end{cases} \qquad (3)\begin{cases} g_{\alpha\beta}: & 2 \\ S\ : & 1 \\ \Omega_{\alpha\beta}: & 0 \\ C^{\alpha}\ : & 1 \end{cases} \qquad (4)\begin{cases} g_{\alpha\beta}: & 3 \\ S\ : & 2 \\ \Omega_{\alpha\beta}: & 1 \\ C^{\alpha}\ : & 2 \end{cases}$$

These maxima orders are compatible with our system.

(b) Our initial data on Σ are, as we know, the values of the $g_{\alpha\beta}$, of their first derviatives and of S. We assume that these data are such that:

1. *The quadratic form* $g_{\lambda\mu} v^{\lambda} v^{\mu}$ *is normal hyperbolic; the hypersurface* Σ *is space-like in each point with respect to the corresponding elementary cone.*

2. *We have on* Σ

$$F^{\rho} = 0, \qquad \text{for } x^0 = 0.$$

3. *The relations* $S^0_{\alpha} = \chi T^0_{\alpha}$ *and the value of* S *define an admissible value for* f *and, thus, values for* p *and the* C^{α}, *with*

$$\frac{f r'_f}{r} \geq 1. \qquad (15\text{-}6)$$

We have the same situation as in §8 for the operators a(1) and a(2) = a(3): to a(1) corresponds the half-cone $\Gamma_X^+(1)$ defined by

$$g^{\lambda\mu}\xi_\lambda\xi_\mu \geq 0,$$

with $\xi(\mathbf{v}) \geq 0$ for $\mathbf{v} \in C_X^+$. To a(2) = a(3) corresponds the half-cone $\Gamma_X^+(2) = \Gamma_X^+(3)$ defined by

$$C^\lambda \xi_\lambda \geq 0, \qquad C^\lambda \in C_X^+.$$

We consider now the half-cone $\hat{\Gamma}_X^+$ defined by means of

$$\left[g^{\lambda\mu} - \left(1 - \frac{fr_f'}{r}\right)\frac{C^\lambda C^\mu}{f^2}\right]\xi_\lambda\xi_\mu \geq 0.$$

This half-cone is exterior to the half-cone $\Gamma_X^+(1)$ and does not cut the plane $C^\lambda\xi_\lambda = 0$, under the assumption (15-6). It follows that the interior of the intersection of $\Gamma_X^+(1)$, $\Gamma_X^+(2) = \Gamma_X^+(3)$, $\Gamma_X^+(4)$ is not empty. This interior is, in fact, the interior of $\Gamma_X^+(1)$. Thus the matrix A is *strictly hyperbolic.*

The equations (15-1) give the values on Σ of the second derivatives of the $g_{\alpha\beta}$, the equations (15-2) the values of the first derivatives of S. The equations (13-7) and (13-8) give, as we know, the first derivatives of the C^α. By differentiation, (15-1) gives the third derivatives of the $g_{\alpha\beta}$ and (15-2) the second derivatives of S. The equations (15-4) give the first derivatives of the $\Omega_{\alpha\beta}$ and (14-7) the second derivatives of the C^α. We have thus obtained the values on Σ of the derivatives of order $\leq s(\sigma) - 1$.

We consider the corresponding Cauchy problem for the *strictly hyperbolic Leray system* (15-1), (15-2), (15-3), (15-4). If the initial data are sufficiently regular, the theorem of Leray shows that *this Cauchy problem has one and only one solution* ($g_{\alpha\beta}$, S, $\Omega_{\alpha\beta}$, C^α).

(c) It is necessary now to prove that ($g_{\alpha\beta}$, S, C^{α}) gives a solution of the system (13-4), (13-6), (13-7), (13-8). We have proved in §13 that, if the Cauchy data are analytic, the system defined by these equations has, under our assumptions, one and only one solution ($g_{\alpha\beta}$, S, C^{α}). This solution, with $\Omega_{\alpha\beta} = \partial_{\alpha} C_{\beta} - \partial_{\beta} C_{\alpha}$, satisfies necessarily the system (15-1), (15-2), (15-3), (15-4) and, according to the choice of the adopted Cauchy data, coincides with the solution of this system given by the theorem of Leray.

A *standard limit process* shows then that this last solution satisfies the system (13-4), (13-6), (13-7), (13-8) in the case where the data are not assumed analytic, but only sufficiently differentiable. According to the general argument of §4, we have thus obtained *a local existence and uniqueness theorem for the Cauchy problem corresponding to the equations (13-2), (13-3), (13-4) for a relativistic thermodynamical perfect fluid.*

16. Another Method

To prove the previous theorem, we will give now a different method where the vorticity tensor does not appear.

(a) The differential system (10-5) of the stream lines can be written

$$f u^{\alpha} \nabla_{\alpha} u^{\beta} - (g^{\alpha\beta} - u^{\alpha} u^{\beta}) \partial_{\alpha} f + \frac{rT}{c^2} g^{\alpha\beta} \partial_{\alpha} S = 0. \tag{16-1}$$

The equation of continuity

$$\nabla_{\beta} (r u^{\beta}) = 0,$$

gives

$$r \nabla_{\beta} u^{\beta} + r'_f u^{\beta} \partial_{\beta} f = 0. \tag{16-2}$$

We take the contracted covariant derivative ∇_β of (16-1). We have thus

$$(g^{\alpha\beta} - u^\alpha u^\beta)\nabla_\alpha\nabla_\beta f - fu^\alpha \nabla_\beta\nabla_\alpha u^\beta - \frac{rT}{c^2} g^{\alpha\beta}\nabla_\alpha\nabla_\beta S$$

$$= A(1 \text{ in } g_{\alpha\beta},\ 1 \text{ in } f,\ 1 \text{ in } S,\ 1 \text{ in } u^\alpha). \qquad (16\text{-}3)$$

But, according to the Ricci identity,

$$\nabla_\beta\nabla_\alpha u^\beta = \nabla_\alpha\nabla_\beta u^\beta + R_{\alpha\rho} u^\rho.$$

From the equation (16-2), it follows that

$$\nabla_\beta(\nabla_\alpha u^\beta) = -\nabla_\alpha\left(\frac{r'_f}{r} u^\beta \partial_\beta f\right) + R_{\alpha\rho} u^\rho,$$

and thus

$$u^\beta\nabla_\beta\nabla_\alpha u^\beta = -u^\alpha u^\beta \frac{r'_f}{r}\nabla_\alpha\nabla_\beta f$$

$$+ B(2 \text{ in } g_{\alpha\beta},\ 1 \text{ in } f,\ 1 \text{ in } S,\ 1 \text{ in } u^\alpha).$$

According to this relation, (16-3) can be written

$$\left[g^{\alpha\beta} - u^\alpha u^\beta\left(1 - \frac{fr'_f}{r}\right)\right]\nabla_\alpha\nabla_\beta f$$

$$= \frac{rT}{c^2} g^{\alpha\beta}\nabla_\alpha\nabla_\beta S$$

$$+ C(2 \text{ in } g_{\alpha\beta},\ 1 \text{ in } f,\ 1 \text{ in } S,\ 1 \text{ in } u^\alpha). \qquad (16\text{-}4)$$

Now we take the derivative of (16-4) along the current lines. According to the action of the operator $u^\gamma\nabla_\gamma$, we have

$$u^\gamma g^{\alpha\beta}\nabla_\gamma\nabla_\alpha\nabla_\beta S = u^\gamma g^{\alpha\beta}\nabla_\alpha\nabla_\beta\nabla_\gamma S$$

$$- R_\gamma{}^\rho u^\gamma \partial_\rho S.$$

Since $u^\gamma \partial_\gamma S = 0$,

$$u^\gamma g^{\alpha\beta} \nabla_\gamma \nabla_\alpha \nabla_\beta S = D(2 \text{ in } g_{\alpha\beta},\ 2 \text{ in } S,\ 2 \text{ in } u^\gamma).$$

We obtain

$$u^\gamma \left[g^{\alpha\beta} - u^\alpha u^\beta \left(1 - \frac{fr'_f}{r}\right)\right] \partial_{\alpha\beta\gamma} f$$

$$= E(3 \text{ in } g_{\alpha\beta},\ 2 \text{ in } f,\ 2 \text{ in } S,\ 2 \text{ in } u^\gamma). \qquad (16\text{-}5)$$

(b) We consider now the differential system (16-1) of the stream lines when we apply the differential operator

$$\left[g^{\lambda\mu} - u^\lambda u^\mu \left(1 - \frac{fr'_f}{r}\right)\right] \nabla_\lambda \nabla_\mu .$$

It follows that

$$fu^\alpha \left[g^{\lambda\mu} - u^\lambda u^\mu \left(1 - \frac{fr'_f}{r}\right)\right] \nabla_\lambda \nabla_\mu \nabla_\alpha u^\beta$$

$$- (g^{\alpha\beta} - u^\alpha u^\beta) \left[g^{\lambda\mu} - u^\lambda u^\mu \left(1 - \frac{fr'_f}{r}\right)\right]$$

$$\times \nabla_\lambda \nabla_\mu \nabla_\alpha f + \frac{rT}{c^2} g^{\alpha\beta} g^{\lambda\mu} \nabla_\lambda \nabla_\mu \nabla_\alpha S$$

$$= F^\beta (3 \text{ in } g_{\alpha\beta},\ 2 \text{ in } f,\ 2 \text{ in } S,\ 2 \text{ in } u^\gamma),$$

where we have used $u^\gamma \partial_\gamma S = 0$. From (16-4), it follows that

$$fu^\gamma \left[g^{\lambda\mu} - u^\lambda u^\mu \left(1 - \frac{fr'_f}{r}\right)\right] \nabla_\lambda \nabla_\mu \nabla_\gamma u^\beta$$

$$- \frac{rT}{c^2} (g^{\alpha\beta} - u^\alpha u^\beta) g^{\lambda\mu} \nabla_\lambda \nabla_\mu \nabla_\alpha S$$

$$+ \frac{rT}{c^2} g^{\alpha\beta} g^{\lambda\mu} \nabla_\lambda \nabla_\mu \nabla_\alpha S$$

$$= G^\beta (3 \text{ in } g_{\alpha\beta},\ 2 \text{ in } f,\ 2 \text{ in } S,\ 2 \text{ in } u^\gamma).$$

According to $u^\alpha \partial_\alpha S = 0$, we have finally

$$u^\gamma \left[g^{\lambda\mu} - u^\lambda u^\mu \left(1 - \frac{fr'_f}{r}\right)\right] \partial_{\lambda\mu\gamma} u^\beta$$

$$= H^\beta (3 \text{ in } g_{\alpha\beta},\ 2 \text{ in S},\ 2 \text{ in } u^\gamma). \qquad (16\text{-}6)$$

(c) Now, we consider as the unknown functions the 10 $g_{\alpha\beta}$, the scalars f and S, and the 4 u^α, which define an arbitrary vector. We have thus 16 unknown functions.

We substitute in the Einstein equations the derivatives of (13-6) along the stream lines. There appears in the right member

$$u^\gamma \nabla_\gamma \left[rfu\alpha u_\beta - \frac{1}{2}\left(rf - \frac{2p}{c^2}\right) g_{\alpha\beta}\right]$$

$$= u^\gamma \nabla_\gamma (rf) u_\alpha u_\beta + rfu^\gamma \nabla_\gamma (u_\alpha u_\beta)$$

$$- \frac{1}{2} g_{\alpha\beta} u^\gamma \nabla_\gamma \left(rf - \frac{2p}{c^2}\right).$$

According to the system (16-1), we have

$$u^\gamma \nabla_\gamma \left[rfu_\alpha u_\beta - \frac{1}{2}\left(rf - \frac{2p}{c^2}\right) g_{\alpha\beta}\right]$$

$$= f_{\alpha\beta} (1 \text{ in } g_{\alpha\beta},\ 1 \text{ in f},\ 1 \text{ in S},\ 0 \text{ in } u^\gamma).$$

We consider thus the partial differential system defined by the derivatives of (13-6) along the current lines:

$$-\tfrac{1}{2} u^\gamma g^{\alpha\beta} \partial_{\alpha\beta\gamma} g_{\lambda\mu}$$

$$= F_{\lambda\mu} (2 \text{ in } g_{\alpha\beta},\ 1 \text{ in f},\ 1 \text{ in S},\ 0 \text{ in } u^\gamma), \qquad (16\text{-}7)$$

by the equation (16-5);

$$u^\gamma\left[g^{\alpha\beta} - u^\alpha u^\beta\left(1 - \frac{fr'_f}{r}\right)\right]\partial_{\alpha\beta\gamma} f$$

$$= E(3 \text{ in } g_{\alpha\beta},\ 2 \text{ in } f,\ 2 \text{ in } S,\ 2 \text{ in } u^\gamma), \qquad (16\text{-}8)$$

by the equation

$$u^\gamma \partial_\gamma S = 0, \qquad (16\text{-}9)$$

and by the system deduced in (b) from the differential system of the current lines:

$$u^\gamma\left[g^{\alpha\beta} - u^\alpha u^\beta\left(1 - \frac{fr'_f}{r}\right)\right]\partial_{\alpha\beta\gamma} u^\lambda$$

$$= H^\lambda (3 \text{ in } g_{\alpha\beta},\ 2 \text{ in } f,\ 2 \text{ in } S,\ 2 \text{ in } u^\gamma). \qquad (16\text{-}10)$$

This system is a Leray system; the matrix A, here 16×16, is that matrix, the diagonal elements of which are respectively

$$a(7) = -\tfrac{1}{2} u^\gamma g^{\alpha\beta} \partial_{\alpha\beta\gamma},$$

$$a(8) = a(10) = u^\gamma\left[g^{\alpha\beta} - u^\alpha u^\beta\left(1 - \frac{fr'_f}{r}\right)\right]\partial_{\alpha\beta\gamma},$$

$$a(9) = u^\gamma \partial_\gamma .$$

This system satisfies the assumptions on the derivatives with the following indices for the unknowns

$$s(g_{\alpha\beta}) = 4, \qquad s(f) = 3, \qquad s(S) = 3, \qquad s(u^\gamma) = 3,$$

and the following indices for the equations

$$t(7) = 2, \qquad t(8) = 1, \qquad t(9) = 3, \qquad t(10) = 1.$$

Indeed a(7) and a(8) = a(10) have the order 3, a(9) has the

order 1. The table giving the maximum order of derivation, corresponding to these indices is the following:

$$(7)\begin{cases} g_{\alpha\beta} : 2 \\ f \quad : 1 \\ S \quad : 1 \\ u^\gamma \quad : 1 \end{cases} \qquad \begin{matrix}(8)\\(10)\end{matrix}\begin{cases} g_{\alpha\beta} : 3 \\ f \quad : 2 \\ S \quad : 2 \\ u^\gamma \quad : 2 \end{cases} \qquad (9)\begin{cases} g_{\alpha\beta} : 1 \\ f \quad : 0 \\ S \quad : 0 \\ u^\gamma \quad : 0 \end{cases}$$

These maxima orders are compatible with our system.

(d) Our initial data on the hypersurface Σ are the values of the potentials $g_{\alpha\beta}$, of their first derivatives, and of S. We suppose that these values satisfy the assumptions of §15.

The equations (13-6) give the values on Σ of the second derivatives of the $g_{\alpha\beta}$; the equation (16-9) gives the values of the first derivatives of S. The equations (13-7) and (13-8) give, as we know, the values of the first derivatives of f and of the u^γ. The equation (16-9) gives, by differentiation, the second derivatives of S, and (16-7) the third derivatives of the $g_{\alpha\beta}$. The equation (16-4) gives the values of the second derivatives of f, and (16-1), by differentiation, the values of the second derivatives of the u^γ. We have obtained thus the values on Σ of the derivatives of order $\leq s(\sigma) - 1$.

We consider the corresponding Cauchy problem for the strictly hyperbolic Leray system (16-7), (16-8), (16-9), (16-10). An argument similar to that of §15 shows that if the initial data are sufficiently regular, *our problem has one and only one solution which is a solution of the first system (13-2), (13-3), (13-4).* We have thus another proof of the theorem of §15.

The principle of this method is specially adapted to the study of the equations of relativistic magnetohydrodynamics (infinite conductivity).

17. Incompressible Thermodynamical Fluid

(a) I say that a relativistic thermodynamical fluid is incompressible if the velocity of its hydrodynamical waves is equal to c, that is, if r(f, S) satisfies

$$\gamma \equiv \frac{fr'_f}{r} = 1. \tag{17-1}$$

We see by integration that this is the case if and only if

$$r = q(S)f, \tag{17-2}$$

where q is a function depending only on S.

Under this assumption, let us study the pressure of the fluid. According to (13-1), we have

$$p'_f = c^2 r = c^2 q(S)f.$$

It follows that there exists a function $\pi(S)$, such that

$$\frac{p}{c^2} = q(S)\frac{f^2}{2} - \pi(S). \tag{17-3}$$

If ρ is the proper energy density, we know that

$$\rho + \frac{p}{c^2} = rf.$$

Thus, we have

$$\rho - \frac{p}{c^2} = rf - 2\frac{p}{c^2} = q(S)f^2 - q(S)f^2 + 2\pi(S),$$

and so we obtain

$$\rho - \frac{p}{c^2} = 2\pi(S). \tag{17-4}$$

Conversely, we assume that $[\rho - (p/c^2)]$ *depends only on* S, that is, $rf - 2(p/c^2)$ depends only on S. By differentiation in f, it follows that

$$fr'_f + r - \frac{2}{c^2} p'_f = 0,$$

and, as $p'_f = c^2 r$, we have

$$fr'_f - r = 0.$$

That is, our fluid is incompressible. We obtain the following theorem.

Theorem. A relativistic thermodynamical fluid is incompressible if and only if the difference $[\rho - (p/c^2)]$ *depends only on* S.

(**b**) According to (17-2), the quotient r/f which depends only on S is constant along the current lines:

$$u^\alpha \partial_\alpha (r/f) = 0. \tag{17-5}$$

From the equation of continuity $\nabla_\alpha (ru^\alpha) = 0$, it follows according to (17-5) that

$$\nabla_\alpha (fu^\alpha) = 0. \tag{17-6}$$

Conversely, if such is the case, we have (17-5) and thus, explicitly

$$(fr'_f - r)u^\alpha \partial_\alpha f = 0.$$

It follows that, apart from the trivial case where all the thermodynamical variables are constant along the current lines (and $\nabla_\alpha u^\alpha = 0$), we have (17-6).

Theorem. If a relativistic thermodynamical fluid is incompressible, its current vector satisfies

$$\delta \mathbf{C} = 0. \tag{17-7}$$

Conversely, if (17-7) holds, either the fluid is incompressible or we have the trivial case where all the thermodynamical variables are constant along the current lines.

(c) Let us consider an incompressible fluid. We have in this case,

$$\Delta \mathbf{C} = (d\delta + \delta d)\mathbf{C},$$

that is, according to (17-7),

$$\Delta \mathbf{C} = \delta\Omega, \tag{17-8}$$

which can be written explicitly,

$$-g^{\alpha\beta}\nabla_\alpha \nabla_\beta C_\lambda + R_{\lambda\rho} C^\rho + \nabla^\alpha \Omega_{\alpha\lambda} = 0. \tag{17-9}$$

This is the present form of (14-8). The system corresponding to the incompressible case is a special case of the considered general case. We have here as operators only

$$g^{\lambda\mu}\partial_{\lambda\mu}, \qquad u^\gamma \partial_\gamma,$$

and their products.

18. Irrotational Motion

(a) The motion of a relativistic thermodynamical perfect fluid is called *irrotational* if its vorticity tensor is null,

$$\Omega = 0,$$

that is, if

$$d\mathbf{C} = 0.$$

There exists *locally* a function φ such that $\mathbf{C} = d\varphi$; φ can be called the *velocity potential*.

Let us assume that the motion is irrotational; from (12-4), it follows that

$$\frac{Tf}{c^2} dS = 0,$$

and we see that it is *necessary that the motion of the fluid should be isentropic* (S = const.).

Conversely, if our fluid is isentropic, Helmholtz equations can be written

$$\mathcal{L}(\mathbf{C})\Omega = 0;$$

let

$$C^{\rho} \nabla_{\rho} \Omega_{\alpha\beta} + \nabla_{\alpha} C^{\rho} \Omega_{\rho\beta} + \nabla_{\beta} C^{\rho} \Omega_{\alpha\rho} = 0.$$

These equations imply the conservation of the irrotational character of the motion: *if Ω is zero on a space-like hypersurface, this tensor is zero everywhere and the motion is irrotational.*

(**b**) It is easy to form, by means of the calculations of §14, the equation corresponding to the velocity potential φ. According to §14, we have

$$\Delta\varphi = \delta d\varphi = \delta\mathbf{C} = i(\mathbf{C})dH.$$

But, from §14 (b) and (c), we have

$$i(\mathbf{C})dH = 2H'_h C^{\alpha} C^{\beta} \nabla_{\alpha} C_{\beta}$$

$$= -\left(1 - \frac{fr'_f}{r}\right) \frac{C^{\alpha} C^{\beta}}{f^2} \nabla_{\alpha} \nabla_{\beta} \varphi.$$

Thus φ satisfies the equation of the hydrodynamical waves:

$$\left[g^{\alpha\beta} - \left(1 - \frac{fr'_f}{r}\right) \frac{C^{\alpha} C^{\beta}}{f^2}\right] \nabla_{\alpha} \nabla_{\beta} \varphi = 0,$$

$$\text{with } C_{\alpha} = \nabla_{\alpha}\varphi. \qquad (18\text{-}1)$$

Chapter 3

CHARGED FLUID WITH A NULL CONDUCTIVITY

In this chapter we introduce an electromagnetic field. After a brief recapitulation of relativistic electrodynamics, we consider the charged perfect fluid with vanishing conductivity. We establish the existence and uniqueness of solutions of the Cauchy problem for this case.

19. The Main Differential System for the Fluid

In this section, our purpose is to study the main system of equations for a charged perfect fluid with a null conductivity in an electromagnetic field.

(**a**) In the considered domain of space-time, we assume that there exists an electromagnetic field *without induction,* defined by a 2-form $\mathbf{F}$ satisfying the Maxwell equations

$$d\mathbf{F} = 0 \tag{19-1}$$

and

$$\delta \mathbf{F} = -\mathbf{J}, \tag{19-2}$$

where $\mathbf{J}$ is the electric current. The equation (19-1) expresses the fact that there exists locally an electromagnetic potential ψ such that $\mathbf{F} = d\psi$. The equation (19-2) can be written explicitly

$$\nabla_\alpha F^{\alpha\beta} = J^\beta . \tag{19-3}$$

From $\delta^2 = 0$, it follows $\delta \mathbf{J} = 0$: the electric current is conservative.

To the electromagnetic field $\mathbf{F}$, we associate the Maxwell energy tensor,

$$\tau_{\alpha\beta} = \tfrac{1}{4} g_{\alpha\beta} (F_{\lambda\mu} F^{\lambda\mu}) - F_{\alpha\rho} F_\beta{}^\rho , \qquad g^{\alpha\beta} \tau_{\alpha\beta} = 0. \tag{19-4}$$

It is well known that it follows from the Maxwell equations by an easy calculation,

$$\nabla_\alpha \tau^\alpha{}_\beta = J^\alpha F_{\alpha\beta} . \tag{19-5}$$

(**b**) The considered domain contains an energy distribution corresponding to a charged thermodynamical perfect fluid and to the electromagnetic field. The metric of the space-time satisfies the Einstein equations.

$$S_{\alpha\beta} = \chi T_{\alpha\beta} , \tag{19-6}$$

where the total energy tensor $T_{\alpha\beta}$ is the sum

$$T_{\alpha\beta} = rfu_\alpha u_\beta - \frac{p}{c^2} g_{\alpha\beta} + \tau_{\alpha\beta} \tag{19-7}$$

of the energy-momentum tensor of the fluid and of the Maxwell tensor of the electromagnetic field. Similarly, to §9 and §10, r is the proper matter density of the fluid, p its pressure, u_α the unitary velocity and f the index of the fluid defined by

$$f = 1 + \frac{i}{c^2} , \tag{19-8}$$

where i is the specific enthalpy. The proper temperature T and the specific entropy are still defined by means of

$$TdS = di - \frac{dp}{r} . \tag{19-9}$$

The electric current **J** is, in general, the sum of two terms corresponding to a convection current and to a conduction current (Ohm's Law). Let

$$J^{\beta} = \epsilon u^{\beta} + \sigma u_{\alpha} F^{\alpha\beta} , \tag{19-10}$$

where ϵ is the proper density of electric charge and σ the conductivity of the fluid. We assume here that the conductivity is null ($\sigma = 0$) and so we have only

$$J^{\beta} = \epsilon u^{\beta} . \tag{19-11}$$

From $\delta \mathbf{J} = 0$, it follows that

$$\nabla_{\beta} (\epsilon u^{\beta}) = 0 . \tag{19-12}$$

20. The Equation of Continuity and the Differential System of the Stream Lines

(**a**) We form the equations of conservation $\nabla_{\alpha} T^{\alpha}{}_{\beta} = 0$, these being consequences of the Einstein equations, with

$$T_{\alpha\beta} = rfu_{\alpha} u_{\beta} - \frac{p}{c^2} g_{\alpha\beta} + \tau_{\alpha\beta} .$$

It follows, according to (19-5), that

$$\nabla_{\alpha} T^{\alpha}{}_{\beta} \equiv \nabla_{\alpha}(rfu^{\alpha}) u_{\beta} + rfu^{\alpha} \nabla_{\alpha} u_{\beta} - \frac{\partial_{\beta} p}{c^2}$$

$$+ J^{\alpha} F_{\alpha\beta} = 0 ;$$

that is, according to (19-11),

$$\nabla_\alpha T^\alpha{}_\beta \equiv \nabla_\alpha(rfu^\alpha)u_\beta + rfu^\alpha \nabla_\alpha u_\beta - \frac{\partial_\beta p}{c^2}$$

$$+ \epsilon u^\alpha F_{\alpha\beta} = 0. \qquad (20\text{-}1)$$

If we multiply by u^β, we obtain the equation of continuity,

$$u^\beta \nabla_\alpha T^\alpha{}_\beta \equiv \nabla_\alpha(rf\,u^\alpha) - \frac{u^\alpha \partial_\alpha p}{c^2} = 0. \qquad (20\text{-}2)$$

According to (19-8) and (19-9), this equation can be written, as in §11,

$$f\nabla_\alpha(ru^\alpha) + \frac{1}{c^2}\, rTu^\alpha \partial_\alpha S = 0. \qquad (20\text{-}3)$$

We assume as before that the motion is locally adiabatic

$$u^\alpha \partial_\alpha S = 0 \qquad (20\text{-}4)$$

or, equivalently, that the matter density is conservative

$$\nabla_\alpha(r\,u^\alpha) = 0. \qquad (20\text{-}5)$$

From (19-12) and (20-5), we deduce that

$$u^\alpha \frac{\partial_\alpha \epsilon}{\epsilon} + \nabla_\alpha u^\alpha = 0, \qquad u^\alpha \frac{\partial_\alpha r}{r} + \nabla_\alpha u^\alpha = 0,$$

and by taking the difference,

$$u^\alpha \partial_\alpha \log(\epsilon/r) = 0.$$

Thus the quotient $k = \epsilon/r$ is constant along the stream lines. We assume that our fluid is charged in a homogeneous way, that is,

$$k = \epsilon/r = \text{a given constant}$$

in the whole of the considered domain of space-time.

(**b**) According to the equation of continuity, (20-1) can be written

$$rfu^{\alpha}\nabla_{\alpha}u^{\beta} = (g^{\alpha\beta} - u^{\alpha}u^{\beta})\frac{\partial_{\alpha}p}{c^2} - \epsilon u^{\alpha}F_{\alpha}^{\ \beta}.$$

Then

$$fu^{\alpha}\nabla_{\alpha}u^{\beta} = (g^{\alpha\beta} - u^{\alpha}u^{\beta})\left(\partial_{\alpha}f - \frac{T\partial_{\alpha}S}{c^2}\right)$$

$$- ku^{\alpha}F_{\alpha}^{\ \beta}, \tag{20-6}$$

which is the differential system of the stream lines.

If the fluid is isentropic, it is possible to translate this differential system in the following way—the stream lines are extremals of the integral,

$$\int (f\,ds + k\psi),$$

where ψ is the electromagnetic potential (see, for example, Lichnerowicz [7], p. 101).

In the general case, we again introduce the metric $\overline{ds}^2 = f^2 ds^2$ and the hydrodynamic current **C** defined by

$$C_{\alpha} = fu_{\alpha}, \qquad C^{\alpha} = fu^{\alpha}. \tag{20-7}$$

We set also

$$\overline{C}^{\alpha} = f^{-1}u^{\alpha}.$$

From (20-6), which can be written in the form

$$u^\alpha \nabla_\alpha u_\beta - (g^\alpha_\beta - u^\alpha u_\beta)\left(\frac{\partial_\alpha f}{f} - \frac{T\partial_\alpha S}{c^2 f}\right)$$

$$+ \frac{k}{f} u^\alpha F_{\alpha\beta} = 0,$$

it follows, according to the lemma of §10, that the differential system of the stream-lines can be written

$$\bar{C}^\alpha \bar{\nabla}_\alpha C_\beta + (g^\alpha_\beta - u^\alpha u_\beta) \frac{T\partial_\alpha S}{c^2 f} + \frac{k}{f} u^\alpha F_{\alpha\beta} = 0,$$

where $\bar{\nabla}_\alpha$ is the covariant derivation in the metric $\overline{ds}^2$; if we multiply by f^2, we obtain

$$C^\alpha \bar{\nabla}_\alpha C_\beta + (g^\alpha_\beta - u^\alpha u_\beta) \frac{Tf}{c^2} \partial_\alpha S + kC^\alpha F_{\alpha\beta} = 0.$$

(20-8)

21. Relativistic Helmholtz Equations

To the current **C**, we associate the 1-form,

$$\mathbf{I} = \mathbf{C} + k\psi \tag{21-1}$$

and its exterior differential,

$$\Pi = d\mathbf{C} + kd\psi = \Omega + k\mathbf{F}, \qquad \Omega = d\mathbf{C}, \tag{21-2}$$

which is called here the total vorticity tensor of the charged fluid.

First, we will transform the differential system of the stream lines to obtain a form in which the vorticity tensor Π occurs in a simple way. From (20-8) and $u^\alpha \partial_\alpha S = 0$, it follows that the system of the stream lines can be written

$$C^{\alpha} \overline{\nabla}_{\alpha} C_{\beta} + \frac{Tf}{c^2} \partial_{\beta} S + k C^{\alpha} F_{\alpha\beta} = 0 . \qquad (21\text{-}3)$$

But, we have seen in §12 that

$$C^{\alpha} \overline{\nabla}_{\alpha} C_{\beta} = C^{\alpha} \Omega_{\alpha\beta} .$$

So (21-3) can be written

$$C^{\alpha} (\Omega_{\alpha\beta} + k F_{\alpha\beta}) + \frac{Tf}{c^2} \partial_{\beta} S = 0 .$$

We obtain for the system of the stream lines

$$i(\mathbf{C}) \Pi = - \frac{Tf}{c^2} dS . \qquad (21\text{-}4)$$

From (21-4), it follows easily, in the isentropic case, the variational translation given for the system of the stream lines.

We obtain the Helmholtz equations for a charged fluid if we note that

$$\mathcal{L}(\mathbf{C}) \Pi = \{d i(\mathbf{C}) + i(\mathbf{C}) d\} \Pi = d i(\mathbf{C}) \Pi .$$

From (21-4), there follow thus the Helmholtz equations,

$$\mathcal{L}(\mathbf{C}) \Pi = -\frac{1}{c^2} d(Tf) \wedge dS , \qquad (21\text{-}5)$$

that is, explicitly,

$$C^{\rho} \nabla_{\rho} \Pi_{\alpha\beta} + \nabla_{\alpha} C^{\rho} \Pi_{\rho\beta} + \nabla_{\beta} C^{\rho} \Pi_{\alpha\beta}$$

$$= -\frac{1}{c^2} [\partial_{\alpha} (Tf) \partial_{\beta} S - \partial_{\beta} (Tf) \partial_{\alpha} S] . \qquad (21\text{-}6)$$

22. Relations between Hydrodynamic Current and Vorticity Tensor

There exists a system of relations between the hydrodynamic current and the total vorticity tensor which is an extension of the relations of the §14. We still have the same equation of continuity. Then

$$\Delta \mathbf{C} = \mathcal{L}(\mathbf{C})H + \delta\Omega , \tag{22-1}$$

where

$$H(h, S) = \log (r/f) , \qquad h = f^2 .$$

(**a**) Similarly, we have

$$\partial_\lambda H = 2H'_h C^\alpha \nabla_\alpha C_\lambda - 2H'_h C^\alpha \Omega_{\alpha\lambda} + H'_S \partial_\lambda S .$$

But, according to (21-4),

$$C^\alpha \Omega_{\alpha\lambda} = -kC^\alpha F_{\alpha\lambda} - \frac{Tf}{c^2} \partial_\lambda S .$$

It follows that

$$\partial_\lambda H = 2H'_h C^\alpha \nabla_\alpha C_\lambda + \left(2H'_h \frac{Tf}{c^2} + H'_h\right) \partial_\lambda S$$

$$+ 2kH'_h C^\alpha F_{\alpha\lambda} . \tag{22-2}$$

We still consider f or h as a function of $g_{\alpha\beta}$ and C^α. From (22-2), we deduce

$$[\mathcal{L}(\mathbf{C})dH]_\lambda = 2H'_h C^\alpha C^\beta \nabla_\alpha \nabla_\beta C_\lambda$$

$$+ \left(2H'_h \frac{Tf}{c^2} + H'_S\right) C^\beta \nabla_\beta \nabla_\lambda S$$

$$+ 2kH'_h C^\alpha C^\beta \nabla_\beta F_{\alpha\lambda}$$

$$+ \varphi_\lambda (1 \text{ in } g_{\alpha\beta}, 1 \text{ in } S, 1 \text{ in } C^\alpha, 1 \text{ in } \psi_\alpha),$$

or, according to $C^\beta \nabla_\beta S = 0$,

$$[\mathcal{L}(\mathbf{C})dH]_\lambda = 2H'_h C^\alpha C^\beta \nabla_\alpha \nabla_\beta C_\lambda + 2kH'_h C^\alpha C^\beta \nabla_\beta F_{\alpha\lambda}$$

$$+ \overline{\varphi}_\lambda (1 \text{ in } g_{\alpha\beta}, 1 \text{ in } S, 1 \text{ in } C^\alpha, 1 \text{ in } \psi_\alpha).$$

(**b**) From the previous relation and (22-1), we deduce by an argument similar to the argument of §14,

$$\left[g^{\alpha\beta} - \left(1 - \frac{fr'_f}{r}\right)\frac{C^\alpha C^\beta}{f^2}\right] \nabla_\alpha \nabla_\beta C_\lambda - R^\rho_\lambda C_\rho$$

$$+ (\delta\Omega)_\lambda - \frac{k}{f^2}\left(1 - \frac{fr'_f}{r}\right) C^\alpha C^\beta \nabla_\beta F_{\alpha\lambda}$$

$$+ \chi_\lambda (1 \text{ in } g_{\alpha\beta}, 1 \text{ in } S, 1 \text{ in } C^\alpha, 1 \text{ in } \psi_\alpha) = 0.$$

But

$$\delta\Omega = \delta\Pi - k\delta\mathbf{F} = \delta\Pi + \frac{k\epsilon}{f}\mathbf{C} = \delta\Pi + \frac{k^2 r}{f}\mathbf{C},$$

and so we obtain the following system,

$$\left[g^{\alpha\beta} - \left(1 - \frac{fr_f'}{c^2}\right)\frac{C^\alpha C^\beta}{f^2}\right]\nabla_\alpha \nabla_\beta C_\lambda - R^\rho_\lambda C_\rho$$

$$+ (\delta\Pi)_\lambda - \frac{k}{f^2}\left(1 - \frac{fr_f'}{r}\right) C^\alpha C^\beta \nabla_\beta F_{\alpha\lambda}$$

$$+ \alpha_\lambda (1 \text{ in } g_{\alpha\beta},\ 1 \text{ in } S,\ 1 \text{ in } C^\alpha,\ 1 \text{ in } \psi_\alpha) = 0 . \tag{22-3}$$

23. The Operator $\Delta^{(h)}$

Let us consider the Laplacian $\Delta\psi$ of a 1-form,

$$\Delta\psi = (d\delta + \delta d)\psi .$$

We search for an expression for $\Delta\psi$, which involves the left members F^ρ of the conditions of harmonicity. We have first

$$(d\delta\psi)_\lambda = -g^{\alpha\beta}\nabla_\lambda \nabla_\alpha \psi_\beta .$$

Let

$$(d\delta\psi)_\lambda = -g^{\alpha\beta}\nabla_\lambda (\partial_\alpha \psi_\beta - \Gamma^\rho_{\alpha\beta}\psi_\rho) .$$

It follows that

$$(d\delta\psi)_\lambda = -g^{\alpha\beta}\partial_{\lambda\alpha}\psi_\beta + \partial_\lambda F^\rho \psi_\rho$$

$$+ \beta_\lambda (1 \text{ in } g_{\alpha\beta},\ 1 \text{ in } \psi_\alpha) .$$

But, we have also

$$(\delta d\psi)_\lambda = -\nabla^\beta(\partial_\beta \psi_\lambda - \partial_\lambda \psi_\beta) = -g^{\alpha\beta}\partial_{\alpha\beta}\psi_\lambda$$

$$+ g^{\alpha\beta}\partial_{\lambda\alpha}\psi_\beta + \gamma_\lambda (1 \text{ in } g_{\alpha\beta}, 1 \text{ in } \psi_\alpha).$$

We deduce by addition

$$(\Delta\psi)_\lambda = -g^{\alpha\beta}\partial_{\alpha\beta}\psi_\lambda$$

$$+ \partial_\lambda F^\rho \psi_\rho + \eta_\lambda (1 \text{ in } g_{\alpha\beta}, 1 \text{ in } \psi_\alpha).$$

We are led to introduce the operator $\Delta^{(h)}$ defined by

$$[\Delta^{(h)}\psi]_\lambda = [\Delta\psi]_\lambda - \partial_\lambda F^\rho \psi_\rho . \tag{23-1}$$

$\Delta^{(h)}$ coincides with Δ in harmonic coordinates and we have

$$[\Delta^{(h)}\psi]_\lambda = -g^{\alpha\beta}\partial_{\alpha\beta}\psi_\lambda + \eta_\lambda (1 \text{ in } g_{\alpha\beta}, 1 \text{ in } \psi_\alpha). \tag{23-2}$$

24. The Equations in Harmonic Coordinates with the Lorentz Condition

(a) Let us consider the main system of relativistic hydrodynamics of a charged perfect fluid. We have the Einstein equations

$$S_{\alpha\beta} = \chi T_{\alpha\beta}, \tag{24-1}$$

where $T_{\alpha\beta}$ is given by (19-7), u_α being unitary. We have the assumption

$$u^\alpha \partial_\alpha S = 0, \tag{24-2}$$

and the Maxwell equations which can be written in terms of the electromagnetic potential ψ:

$$(\delta d\psi)_\lambda = -kru_\lambda, \qquad k = \text{const.} \tag{24-3}$$

We denote this system by (I).

(**b**) The electromagnetic potential ψ is defined up to a change of gauge. The Lorentz condition $\delta\psi = 0$ plays here a role similar to the harmonicity conditions.

If a solution of the system (I) satisfies $F^\rho = 0$ and $\delta\psi = 0$, it is a solution of the system defined by

$$R^{(h)}_{\alpha\beta} = \chi\,(T_{\alpha\beta} - \tfrac{1}{2}g_{\alpha\beta}T), \tag{24-4}$$

the equation

$$u^\alpha \partial_\alpha S = 0, \tag{24-5}$$

the Maxwell equations written in the form

$$[\Delta^{(h)}\psi]_\lambda = -kru_\lambda, \tag{24-6}$$

the conditions of conservation

$$\nabla_\alpha T^\alpha_\beta = 0, \tag{24-7}$$

and finally by the condition of conservation of J, which is here equivalent to

$$\nabla_\alpha(ru^\alpha) = 0. \tag{24-8}$$

We denote this system by (II).

(**c**) Conversely, let us consider a solution of the system (II) corresponding to initial data on a space-like hypersurface Σ (with the local equation $x^0 = 0$) such that:

$$F^{\rho} = 0, \qquad \text{for } x^0 = 0 \tag{24-9}$$

and

$$\delta\psi = 0, \qquad \text{for } x^0 = 0, \tag{24-10}$$

where the left members depend only on the $g_{\alpha\beta}$ and the first derivatives of the $g_{\alpha\beta}$, as well as on the ψ_α and their first derivatives, the values of which are assumed known on Σ. But we know that S^0_α and $(\delta\, d\psi)^0$ depend only on these data on Σ. We assume, moreover, that for our solution,

$$S^0_\alpha = \chi T^0_\alpha, \qquad \text{for } x^0 = 0 \tag{24-11}$$

and

$$(\delta\, d\psi)^0 = -kru^0, \qquad \text{for } x^0 = 0. \tag{24-12}$$

If such is the case, we know, according to the argument of §4, that

$$\partial_0 F^{\rho} = 0, \qquad \text{for } x^0 = 0. \tag{24-13}$$

Similarly, it follows from (24-13) that we have on Σ

$$[\Delta\psi]^0 = [\Delta^{(h)}\psi]^0 = -kru^0$$

and, according to (24-12) and (24-10),

$$(d\delta\psi)^0 = g^{00}(d\delta\psi)_0 = 0.$$

Thus we have

$$(d\delta\psi)_0 = 0. \tag{24-14}$$

(d) Now an argument similar to the argument of §4 shows that the F^{ρ} satisfy the system,

$$g^{\alpha\beta}\partial_{\alpha\beta}F^{\rho} + A^{\rho\alpha}_{\beta}\partial_{\alpha}F^{\beta} = 0, \tag{24-15}$$

where $A^{\rho\alpha}_{\beta}$ are some functions of $g_{\alpha\beta}$ and their first derivatives. From (24-6), i.e., from

$$[\Delta\psi]_{\lambda} - \partial_{\lambda}F^{\rho}\psi_{\rho} = -kru_{\lambda},$$

it follows by the action of δ,

$$\Delta\delta\psi + \nabla^{\lambda}\partial_{\lambda}F^{\rho}\psi_{\rho} + \partial_{\lambda}F^{\rho}\nabla^{\lambda}\psi_{\rho} = 0,$$

that is,

$$\Delta\delta\psi + g^{\alpha\beta}\partial_{\alpha\beta}F^{\rho}\psi_{\rho} + B^{\beta}_{\alpha}\partial_{\alpha}F^{\beta} = 0, \tag{24-16}$$

where the B^{α}_{β} are functions of the $g_{\alpha\beta}$, the ψ_{α} and their first derivatives. There exists one and only one solution (F^{ρ}, $\delta\psi$) of (24-15), (24-16) corresponding to the data on Σ: $F^{\rho} = 0$, $\partial_0 F^{\rho} = 0$, $\delta\psi = 0$, $\partial_0\delta\psi = 0$, and it is the zero solution. It follows that our solution of the system (II) satisfies the system (I). We have the following result:

Theorem. Each solution of the system (II), such that on Σ the conditions (24-9), (24-10), (24-11), (24-12) are satisfied, is a solution of the system (I).

25. Differential System of the Stream Lines Deduced for the System (II)

We assume that the system (II) is satisfied and we seek a corresponding differential system for the stream lines. From the conditions of conservation

$$\nabla_{\alpha}T^{\alpha}_{\beta} \equiv \nabla_{\alpha}\left(rfu^{\alpha}u_{\beta} - \frac{p}{c^2}g^{\alpha}_{\beta} + \tau^{\alpha}_{\beta}\right) = 0,$$

it follows that

$$\nabla_\alpha (rfu^\alpha) u_\beta + rfu^\alpha \nabla_\alpha u_\beta - \frac{\partial_\beta p}{c^2} + \nabla_\alpha \tau^\alpha_\beta = 0 . \tag{25-1}$$

From (19-5) and (19-2), we deduce

$$\nabla_\alpha \tau^\alpha_\beta = -(d\psi)_{\rho\beta} (\delta d\psi)^\rho ,$$

that is, according to the definition of $\Delta^{(h)}$,

$$\nabla_\alpha \tau^\alpha_\beta = -(d\psi)^\rho{}_\beta \, [(\Delta^{(h)} \psi)_\rho + \partial_\rho F^\sigma \psi_\sigma - (d\delta\psi)_\rho] .$$

From (24-6), it follows that

$$\nabla_\alpha \tau^\alpha_\beta = (d\psi)^\rho{}_\beta [kru_\rho - \partial_\rho F^\sigma \psi_\sigma + (d\delta\psi)_\rho] .$$

We obtain for (25-1), according to (24-8),

$$rfu^\alpha \nabla_\alpha u_\beta + ru^\alpha u_\beta \partial_\alpha f - \left(r \partial_\beta f - \frac{T}{c^2} \partial_\beta S \right)$$

$$+ (d\psi)^\rho{}_\beta [kru_\rho - \partial_\rho F^\sigma \psi_\sigma + (d\partial\psi)_\rho = 0 . \tag{25-2}$$

If we multiply this equation by u^β, we obtain, according to $u^\beta \partial_\beta S = 0$,

$$u^\beta d\psi^\rho{}_\beta [-\partial_\rho F^\sigma \psi_\sigma + (d\delta\psi)_\rho] = 0 , \tag{25-3}$$

and so (25-2) can be written

$$rfu^{\alpha} \nabla_{\alpha} u_{\beta} - (g^{\alpha}_{\beta} - u^{\alpha} u_{\beta})\left(r\partial_{\alpha} f - \frac{rT}{c^2} \partial_{\alpha} S\right)$$

$$+ (g^{\alpha}_{\beta} - u^{\alpha} u_{\beta}) d\psi^{\rho}_{\alpha}$$

$$\times [kru_{\rho} - \partial_{\rho} F^{\sigma} \psi_{\sigma} + (d\delta\psi)_{\rho}] = 0, \tag{25-4}$$

which is the differential system that we had sought.

26. Characteristics of the System—Analytic Cauchy Problem

We still take f and S as thermodynamical variables and we assume that r is a known function of f and S,

$$r = r(f, S).$$

We always have (13-1).

Our purpose is to study the Cauchy problem corresponding to the system (II) for data such that (24-11) and (24-12) are satisfied.

(a) On the hypersurface Σ, with the local equation $x^0 = 0$, we are given the values of the $g_{\alpha\beta}$ (with $g^{00} \neq 0$), the values of the ψ_{α}, and the values of their first derivatives. The quantities $(S^0_{\alpha} - x\tau^0_{\alpha})$ are known on Σ. Similarly to §13, we have

$$u_{\alpha} = \frac{S^0_{\alpha} - x\tau^0_{\alpha} + x\frac{p}{c^2} g^0_{\alpha}}{\Omega^0(p)}$$

and

$$u^0 = \frac{S^{00} - \chi\tau^{00} + \chi\frac{p}{c^2}g^{00}}{\Omega^0(p)} \qquad \chi rf = \frac{[\Omega^0(p)]^2}{S^{00} - \chi\tau^{00} + \chi\frac{p}{c^2}g^{00}}, \tag{26-1}$$

where we set

$$[\Omega^0(p)]^2 = g^{\alpha\beta}\left(S^0_\alpha - \chi\tau^0_\alpha + \chi\frac{p}{c^2}g^0_\alpha\right)$$

$$\times\left(S^0_\beta - \chi\tau^0_\beta + \chi\frac{p}{c^2}g^0_\beta\right) > 0. \tag{26-2}$$

Here p plays the part of a parameter. By differentiation of (26-2), we have

$$\Omega^0(p)\frac{d\Omega^0(p)}{dp} = \frac{\chi}{c^2}\left(S^{00} - \chi\tau^{00} + \chi\frac{p}{c^2}g^{00}\right)$$

and according to (26-1),

$$\frac{d\Omega^0(p)}{dp} = \frac{\chi}{c^2}u^0 \neq 0.$$

According to (24-12), $v^0 = ru^0$ is known on Σ. To calculate f and S on Σ, we consider the two equations

$$\chi v^0 f - \Omega^0(p) = 0 \tag{26-3}$$

and

$$\left(S^{00} - \chi\tau^{00} + \chi\frac{p}{c^2}g^{00}\right)rf - \chi(v^0)^2f^2 = 0. \tag{26-4}$$

The Jacobian of these equations with respect to f and S is given by

$$\begin{vmatrix} \chi v^0 - \chi r u^0 = 0 & -\frac{\chi}{c^2} u^0 \frac{\partial p}{\partial S} \\ u^0 \Omega^0(p) r'_f + \chi r^2 (g^{00} - (u^0)^2) & B \end{vmatrix}$$

(where B is a convenient quantity) and it is different from zero, if

$$\chi r f r'_f (u^0)^2 + \chi r^2 [g^{00} - (u^0)^2] \neq 0,$$

that is, if

$$g^{00} - (u^0)^2 \left(1 - \frac{f r'_f}{r}\right) \neq 0.$$

This is the same condition as in §13. We can consider as known the values on Σ of f and S satisfying (26-3) and (26-4) and such that thc Jacobian is different from zero. The values of r, p, T and the values of the u_α defining a unitary vector are then known.

(b) The system (II) gives the equation

$$\nabla_\alpha (r u^\alpha) = r \nabla_\alpha u^\alpha + u^\alpha \partial_\alpha r = 0. \tag{26-5}$$

The system of the stream lines (25-4) gives

$$r f u^\alpha \nabla_\alpha u^\beta - (g^{\alpha\beta} - u^\alpha u^\beta) \left(r \partial_\alpha f - \frac{rT}{c^2} \partial_\alpha S\right)$$
$$+ (g^{\alpha\beta} - u^\alpha u^\beta)(d\psi)^\rho_\alpha$$
$$\times [k r u_\rho - \partial_\rho F^\sigma \psi_\sigma + (d\delta\psi)_\rho] = 0.$$

(26-6)

From (26-6) $u^\alpha u^\beta \nabla_\alpha u_\beta = 0$, and so u_β, which is initially unitary, remains unitary.

We suppose that our initial data are given in terms of formal series. Since $g^{00} \neq 0$, the equations (24-4) give the values on Σ of the derivatives $\partial_{00} g_{\alpha\beta}$ and (24-6) gives the values of the derivatives $\partial_{00} \psi_\alpha$. The equation (24-5) gives, for $u^0 \neq 0$, the value of $\partial_0 S$.

The values on Σ of $\partial_0 u^0$ and $\partial_0 f$ are obtained by the consideration of equations which have the same form as (13-9) and (13-10), and which are deduced from (26-5) and (26-6) for $\beta = 0$. Under the assumed condition $\partial_0 f$, $\partial_0 u^0$ and then the $\partial_0 u^i (i = 1, 2, 3)$ are known on Σ. The same conditions are available for the determination of the successive derivatives.

Thus, under our assumptions,

$$g^{00} \neq 0, \qquad u^0 \neq 0, \qquad g^{00} - (u^0)^2 \left(1 - \frac{f r'_f}{r}\right) \neq 0,$$

we obtain one and only one solution in terms of formal series. *In the analytic case, we obtain this one and only one analytic solution of the Cauchy problem corresponding to the system (II).* The corresponding characteristic hypersurfaces are the same as in the case where we have a null electromagnetic field.

We see that, in the case where the conductivity is null, there exists no action of the electromagnetic field on the hydrodynamic waves.

27. Helmholtz Equations Deduced from the System (II)

If we consider the calculations of §20, we see that the system (25-4) of the stream lines deduced from the system (II) can be written (with $\mathbf{F} = d\psi$):

$$C^\alpha \overline{\nabla}_\alpha C_\beta + \frac{Tf}{c^2} \partial_\beta S + kC^\alpha F_{\alpha\beta} - X^\alpha F_{\alpha\beta} = 0, \tag{27-1}$$

where we set

$$X_\rho = \frac{f}{r} [\partial_\rho F^\sigma \psi_\sigma - (d\delta\psi)_\rho]. \tag{27-2}$$

We have thus from (27-1),

$$C^{\alpha}(\Omega_{\alpha\beta} + kF_{\alpha\beta}) + \frac{Tf}{c^2}\partial_{\beta}S - X^{\alpha}F_{\alpha\beta} = 0, \qquad (27\text{-}3)$$

that is,

$$i(\mathbf{C})\,\Pi = -\frac{Tf}{c^2}\,dS + i(\mathbf{X})\,\mathbf{F}.$$

We consider now

$$\mathcal{L}(\mathbf{C})\,\Pi = di(\mathbf{C})\,\Pi,$$

and, substituting, we obtain

$$\mathcal{L}(\mathbf{C})\,\Pi = -\frac{1}{c^2}\,d(Tf \wedge dS) + di(\mathbf{X})\,\mathbf{F}, \qquad (27\text{-}4)$$

that is,

$$C^{\rho}\nabla_{\rho}\Pi_{\alpha\beta} + \nabla_{\alpha}C^{\rho}\Pi_{\rho\beta} + \nabla_{\beta}C^{\rho}\Pi_{\alpha\rho}$$

$$= -\frac{1}{c^2}[\partial_{\alpha}(Tf)\partial_{\beta}S - \partial_{\beta}(Tf)\partial_{\alpha}S]$$

$$+ \partial_{\alpha}(X^{\rho}F_{\rho\beta}) - \partial_{\beta}(X^{\rho}F_{\rho\alpha}). \qquad (27\text{-}5)$$

28. Relations between Hydrodynamic Current and Vorticity Tensor Deduced from the System (II)

(a) From $\nabla_{\alpha}(ru^{\alpha}) = 0$, we deduce always

$$\delta\mathbf{C} = i(\mathbf{C})\,dH, \qquad H = \log r/f.$$

With the notations of §22, we have

$$\Delta\mathbf{C} = \mathcal{L}(\mathbf{C})\,dH + \delta\Omega \qquad (28\text{-}1)$$

and

$$\partial_\lambda H = 2H'_h C^\alpha \nabla_\alpha C_\lambda - 2H'_h C^\alpha \Omega_{\alpha\lambda} + H'_S \partial_\lambda S .$$

But from (27-3), it follows that

$$C^\alpha \Omega_{\alpha\lambda} = -kC^\alpha F_{\alpha\lambda} - \frac{Tf}{c^2} \partial_\lambda S + X^\alpha F_{\alpha\lambda},$$

and so we have

$$\partial_\lambda H = 2H'_h C^\alpha \nabla_\alpha C_\lambda + \left(2H'_h \frac{Tf}{c^2} + H'_S\right) \partial_\lambda S$$

$$+ 2k H'_h C^\alpha F_{\alpha\lambda} - 2H'_h X^\alpha F_{\alpha\lambda} . \qquad (28\text{-}2)$$

In the following part, we consider as variables the $g_{\alpha\beta}$, S, the $\Pi_{\alpha\beta}$, the C^α, the ψ_α, the F^ρ and $\delta\psi$; f and h are considered as functions of the $g_{\alpha\beta}$ and the C^α. From (28-2), we deduce

$$[\mathfrak{L}(\mathbf{C})\, dH]_\lambda = 2H'_h C^\alpha C^\beta \nabla_\alpha \nabla_\beta C_\lambda$$

$$+ \left(2H'_h \frac{Tf}{c^2} + H'_S\right) C^\beta \nabla_\beta \nabla_\lambda S$$

$$+ \varphi_\lambda (1 \text{ in } g_{\alpha\beta}, 1 \text{ in } S,$$

$$1 \text{ in } C^\alpha, 2 \text{ in } \psi_\alpha, 2 \text{ in } F^\rho, 2 \text{ in } \delta\psi),$$

or according to $C^{\beta}\partial_{\beta}S = 0$,

$$[\mathfrak{L}(\mathbf{C})\,dH]_{\lambda} = 2H'_h C^{\alpha} C^{\beta} \nabla_{\alpha} \nabla_{\beta} C_{\lambda}$$

$$+ \overline{\varphi}_{\lambda}(1 \text{ in } g_{\alpha\beta},\ 1 \text{ in } S,\ 1 \text{ in } C^{\alpha},$$

$$2 \text{ in } \psi_{\alpha},\ 2 \text{ in } F^{\rho},\ 2 \text{ in } \delta\psi).$$

(**b**) By an argument similar to the argument of §14 and §22, we obtain

$$[g^{\alpha\beta} + 2H'_h C^{\alpha} C^{\beta}]\nabla_{\alpha} \nabla_{\beta} C_{\lambda} + (\delta\Omega)_{\lambda}$$

$$+ \chi_{\lambda}\ (2 \text{ in } g_{\alpha\beta},\ 1 \text{ in } S,\ 1 \text{ in } C^{\alpha},\ 2 \text{ in } \psi_{\alpha},$$

$$2 \text{ in } F^{\rho},\ \ 2 \text{ in } \delta\psi) = 0.$$

But

$$\delta\Omega = \delta\Pi - k\delta d\psi = \delta\Pi - k(\Delta\psi - d\delta\psi),$$

and thus

$$(\delta\Omega)_{\lambda} = (\delta\Pi)_{\lambda} - k[(\Delta^{(h)}\psi)_{\lambda} + \partial_{\lambda} F^{\sigma}\psi_{\sigma} - (d\delta\psi)_{\lambda}]$$

and

$$(\delta\Omega)_{\lambda} = (\delta\Pi)_{\lambda} + k\left[\frac{kr}{f} C_{\lambda} - \partial_{\lambda} F^{\sigma}\psi_{\sigma} + (d\delta\psi)_{\lambda}\right].$$

We obtain thus the following system

$$\left[g^{\alpha\beta} - \left(1 - \frac{fr'_f}{r}\right)\frac{C^\alpha C^\beta}{f^2}\right]\nabla_\alpha \nabla_\beta C_\lambda$$

$$+ (\delta\Pi)_\lambda + \alpha_\lambda(2 \text{ in } g_{\alpha\beta},\ 1 \text{ in } S,\ 1 \text{ in } C^\alpha,$$

$$2 \text{ in } \psi_\alpha,\ 2 \text{ in } F^\rho,\ 2 \text{ in } \delta\psi) = 0. \tag{28-3}$$

(c) By the action of the operator $C^\rho\nabla_\rho$, we have

$$C^\rho\nabla_\rho(\delta\Pi)_\lambda = -C^\rho\nabla_\rho\nabla_\alpha \Pi^\alpha{}_\lambda$$

and, according to the Helmholtz equations (27-5), we obtain by an argument similar to the argument of §14,

$$C^\rho\nabla_\rho(\delta\Pi)_\lambda = \beta_\lambda(2 \text{ in } g_{\alpha\beta},\ 2 \text{ in } S,\ 1 \text{ in } \Pi_{\alpha\beta},$$

$$2 \text{ in } C^\alpha,\ 3 \text{ in } \psi_\alpha,\ 3 \text{ in } F^\rho,\ 3 \text{ in } \delta\psi).$$

We have thus deduced from the system (28-3) the following system:

$$C^\rho\left[g^{\alpha\beta} - \left(1 - \frac{fr'_f}{r}\right)\frac{C^\alpha C^\beta}{f^2}\right]\partial_{\rho\alpha\beta} C^\lambda$$

$$= \gamma^\lambda(3 \text{ in } g_{\alpha\beta},\ 2 \text{ in } S,\ 1 \text{ in } \Pi_{\alpha\beta},$$

$$2 \text{ in } C^\alpha,\ 3 \text{ in } \psi_\alpha,\ 3 \text{ in } F^\rho,\ 3 \text{ in } \delta\psi). \tag{28-4}$$

29. Existence and Uniqueness Theorem

(a) Our unknown functions are here the 10 $g_{\alpha\beta}$, S, the 6 $\Pi_{\alpha\beta}$, the 4 C^α, the 4 ψ_α, the 4 F^ρ and $\delta\psi$, that is, 30 unknown functions. We consider the partial differential system defined by:

(i) the equations

$$R^{(h)}_{\alpha\beta} = \chi\left[r\frac{C_\alpha C_\beta}{f^2} - \frac{1}{2}\left(rf - \frac{2p}{c^2}\right)g_{\alpha\beta} + \tau_{\alpha\beta}\right]; \qquad (29\text{-}1)$$

(ii) the equation corresponding to the entropy,

$$C^\alpha \partial_\alpha S = 0; \qquad (29\text{-}2)$$

(iii) the Helmholtz equations deduced from the system (II),

$$C^\rho \partial_\rho \Pi_{\alpha\beta} = \varphi_{\alpha\beta}(1 \text{ in } g_{\alpha\beta},\ 1 \text{ in } S,\ 0 \text{ in } \Pi_{\alpha\beta},$$

$$1 \text{ in } C^\alpha,\ 2 \text{ in } \psi_\alpha,\ 2 \text{ in } F^\rho,\ 2 \text{ in } \partial\psi); \qquad (29\text{-}3)$$

(iv) the equations (28-4),

$$C^\rho\left[g^{\alpha\beta} - \left(1 - \frac{fr'_f}{r}\right)\frac{C^\alpha C^\beta}{f^2}\right]\partial_{\rho\alpha\beta} C^\lambda$$

$$= \gamma^\lambda(3 \text{ in } g_{\alpha\beta},\ 2 \text{ in } S,\ 1 \text{ in } \Pi_{\alpha\beta},\ 2 \text{ in } C^\alpha,\ 3 \text{ in } \psi_\alpha,$$

$$3 \text{ in } F^\rho,\ 3 \text{ in } \delta\psi); \qquad (29\text{-}4)$$

(v) the Maxwell equations (24-6),

$$-g^{\alpha\beta}\partial_{\alpha\beta}\psi_\lambda = -kru_\lambda - \delta_\lambda(1 \text{ in } g_{\alpha\beta},\ 1 \text{ in } \psi_\alpha); \tag{29-5}$$

(vi) the equations (24-15),

$$-g^{\alpha\beta}\partial_{\alpha\beta}F^\rho = \alpha^\rho(1 \text{ in } g_{\alpha\beta},\ 1 \text{ in } F^\rho); \tag{29-6}$$

(vii) and the equation (24-16) which can be written, according to (29-6),

$$-g^{\alpha\beta}\partial_{\alpha\beta}(\delta\psi) = \zeta(1 \text{ in } g_{\alpha\beta},\ 1 \text{ in } \psi_\alpha,\ 1 \text{ in } F^\rho,\ 1 \text{ in } \delta\psi). \tag{29-7}$$

We denote by (III) this system. The system (III) is a Leray system; the matrix A, here 30 × 30, has the nonzero diagonal elements[1]:

$$a(1) = a(5) = a(6) = a(7) = -g^{\alpha\beta}\partial_{\alpha\beta},$$

$$a(2) = a(3) = C^\rho\partial_\rho,$$

$$a(4) = C^\rho\left[g^{\alpha\beta} - \left(1 - \frac{fr'_f}{r}\right)\frac{C^\alpha C^\beta}{f^2}\right]\partial_{\rho\alpha\beta}.$$

The system satisfies the assumptions on the derivatives with the following indices for the unknowns:

[1] The notation is similar to the notation of §8 and §15.

$$s(g_{\alpha\beta}) = 4, \qquad s(S) = 3, \qquad s(\Pi_{\alpha\beta}) = 2,$$

$$s(C^{\alpha}) = 3, \qquad s(\psi_{\alpha}) = 4, \qquad s(F^{\rho}) = 4,$$

$$s(\delta\psi) = 4,$$

and the following indices for the equations:

$$t(1) = 3, \qquad t(2) = 3, \qquad t(3) = 2, \qquad t(4) = 1,$$

$$t(5) = 3, \qquad t(6) = 3, \qquad t(7) = 3.$$

Indeed a(1), a(5), a(6), a(7) have the order 2, a(2) and a(3) the order 1, a(4) the order 3. The table giving the maximum order of derivation for these indices is the following:

$$\begin{matrix}(1)\\(5)\\(6)\\(7)\end{matrix}\left\{\begin{array}{lcl} g_{\alpha\beta} & : & 1 \\ S & : & 0 \\ \Pi_{\alpha\beta} & : & -1 \\ C^{\alpha} & : & 0 \\ \psi_{\alpha} & : & 1 \\ F^{\rho} & : & 1 \\ \delta\psi & : & 1 \end{array}\right. \qquad (2)\left\{\begin{array}{lcl} g_{\alpha\beta} & : & 1 \\ S & : & 0 \\ \Pi_{\alpha\beta} & : & -1 \\ C^{\alpha} & : & 0 \\ \psi_{\alpha} & : & 1 \\ F^{\rho} & : & 1 \\ \delta\psi & : & 1 \end{array}\right.$$

$$(3)\left\{\begin{array}{lcl} g_{\alpha\beta} & : & 2 \\ S & : & 1 \\ \Pi_{\alpha\beta} & : & 0 \\ C^{\alpha} & : & 1 \\ \psi_{\alpha} & : & 2 \\ F^{\rho} & : & 2 \\ \delta\psi & : & 2 \end{array}\right. \qquad (4)\left\{\begin{array}{lcl} g_{\alpha\beta} & : & 3 \\ S & : & 2 \\ \Pi_{\alpha\beta} & : & 1 \\ C^{\alpha} & : & 2 \\ \psi_{\alpha} & : & 3 \\ F^{\rho} & : & 3 \\ \delta\psi & : & 3 \end{array}\right.$$

These maxima orders are compatible with the system (III).

(**b**) Our initial data on the hypersurface Σ are the values of the $g_{\alpha\beta}$, of ψ_α and of their first derivatives. We assume that:

1. *The quadratic form* $g_{\lambda\mu} v^\lambda v^\mu$ *is normal hyperbolic; the hypersurface* Σ *is space-like in each point with respect to the corresponding elementary cone.*
2. *We have on* Σ

$$F^\rho = 0, \qquad \delta\psi = 0, \qquad \text{for } x^0 = 0.$$

3. *The relations* $S^0_\alpha = \chi T^0_\alpha$ *and* $(\delta d\psi)^0 = -kru^0$ *define admissible values for* f *and* S *and, thus, values for* p *and the* C^α, *with*

$$\gamma \equiv \frac{fr'_f}{r} \geq 1.$$

We have the same situation as in §15 and the matrix A is *strictly hyperbolic.*

The equations (29-1) determine the values on Σ of the second derivatives of $g_{\alpha\beta}$; (29-2) the values of the first derivatives of S; (29-5) the values of the second derivatives of the ψ_α. Since $\partial_0 F^\rho = 0$, $\partial_0 \delta\psi = 0$ on Σ, (29-6) and (29-7) give respectively the values of the second derivatives F^ρ and $\delta\psi$. The equations (26-5) and (26-6) give, as we know, the first derivatives of C^α. By a differentiation, equations (29-1) give the third derivatives of the $g_{\alpha\beta}$, (29-2) the second derivatives of S, (29-5) the third derivatives of ψ_α, (29-6) and (29-7) the third derivatives of F^ρ and $\delta\psi$. The equations (29-3) give the values of the first derivatives of $\Pi_{\alpha\beta}$ and (28-3) the second derivatives of C_α. We know thus the values on Σ of the derivatives of order $\leq s(\sigma) - 1$.

We thus obtain a Cauchy problem for the system (III) which is a *strictly hyperbolic Leray system.* If the initial data are sufficiently regular, the theorem of Leray shows that *this Cauchy problem has one and only one solution*

$$g_{\alpha\beta},\ S,\ \Pi_{\alpha\beta},\ C^{\alpha},\ \psi_{\alpha},\ F^{\rho} = 0,\ \delta\psi = 0.$$

An argument similar to the argument of § 15(c) shows that, with our Cauchy data, this solution is a solution of the system (II). Since $F^{\rho} = 0$, $\delta\psi = 0$, we have a solution of the system (I) in harmonic coordinates with a potential ψ satisfying the Lorentz condition.

We have thus obtained *a local existence and uniqueness theorem for the Cauchy problem corresponding to the main system (I) of the equations of a charged perfect fluid with a null conductivity.*

Chapter 4

RELATIVISTIC MAGNETOHYDRODYNAMICS

In Chapter 4 we consider perfect fluids with electromagnetic induction, but having *infinite conductivity*. We formulate first of all relativistic electrodynamics in the presence of induction. Then, the full system of equations governing the motion of the fluid, the electromagnetic field, and the gravitational field is derived. It is shown that these equations have one and only one solution, if the proper Cauchy data are given. Our equations are shown to yield two characteristic types of waves: Alfven waves and hydrodynamical waves. Finally, the simpler special case of an incompressible fluid is analyzed in greater detail.

30. Electromagnetic Field with Induction

(**a**) Inside matter, a general electromagnetic field is defined by two 2-forms **H** and **G**, that is to say by two skew-symmetric tensor fields of order 2. The tensor **H** is called here *the electric field-magnetic induction tensor* and the tensor **G** *the electric induction-magnetic field tensor*.

Let ***H** and ***G** be the dual 2-forms of **H** and **G** in the space-time V_4, where we have chosen *an orientation*. If η is the volume element 4-form of V_4 corresponding to this orientation, we have

$$(^*H)_{\alpha\beta} = \tfrac{1}{2}\,\eta_{\alpha\beta\gamma\delta}\,H^{\gamma\delta}, \qquad (^*G)_{\alpha\beta} = \tfrac{1}{2}\,\eta_{\alpha\beta\gamma\delta}\,G^{\gamma\delta}. \quad (30\text{-}1)$$

It is well known that, if we consider p-forms on a Riemannian manifold V_n, we have

$$*^2 = \frac{g}{|g|}(-1)^{p(n-p)}.$$

Here, with our signature for V_4, we have for the 2-forms: $*^2 = -1$. Thus

$$**\mathbf{H} = -\mathbf{H}, \qquad **\mathbf{G} = -\mathbf{G}. \tag{30-2}$$

If $\mathbf{u}$ is a unitary vector at $x \in V_4$, defining a time-like direction in this point, we set

$$\begin{cases} e_\beta = u^\alpha H_{\alpha\beta}, & d_\beta = u^\alpha G_{\alpha\beta}, \\ b_\beta = u^\alpha (*H)_{\alpha\beta}, & h_\beta = u^\alpha (*G)_{\alpha\beta}. \end{cases} \tag{30-3}$$

It is clear that these four vectors are orthogonal to $\mathbf{u}$

$$u^\alpha e_\alpha = u^\alpha d_\alpha = u^\alpha b_\alpha = u^\alpha h_\alpha = 0.$$

The vectors $\mathbf{e}$ and $\mathbf{d}$ are called, respectively, the *electric field* (or intensity) and the *electric induction* (or displacement) corresponding to the time-like direction $\mathbf{u}$. The vectors $\mathbf{h}$ and $\mathbf{b}$ are called, respectively, the *magnetic field* (or intensity) and the *magnetic induction* corresponding to $\mathbf{u}$. We will see, in a moment, that $\mathbf{e}$ and $\mathbf{b}$ determine $\mathbf{H}$ and that $\mathbf{d}$ and $\mathbf{h}$ determine $\mathbf{G}$.

(**b**) Let us consider at $x \in V_4$ an orthonormalized frame $\{\mathbf{v}_{(\rho)}\}$ such that $\mathbf{v}_{(0)} = \mathbf{u}$; $\{\mathbf{v}_{(\rho)}\}$ is a *rest frame* with respect to $\mathbf{u}$. In this frame, the components e_0, d_0, b_0, h_0 of our four vectors are zero, and we have

$$\begin{cases} e_i = H_{oi}, & d_i = G_{oi}, \\ b_i = (*H)_{oi}, & h_i = (*G)_{oi}, \end{cases} \tag{30-4}$$

where the Latin suffixes take the values (1, 2, 3). It follows that

$$\begin{cases} e^i = H^{oi}, & d^i = G^{oi}, \\ b^i = (*H)^{oi}, & h^i = (*G)^{oi}. \end{cases} \tag{30-5}$$

But, according to the definition of the operator $*$, we have

$$\begin{cases} (*H)_{oi} = \frac{1}{2}\eta_{oijk} H^{jk}, & (*G)_{oi} = \frac{1}{2}\eta_{oijk} G^{jk} \\ H_{oi} = -\frac{1}{2}\eta_{oijk} (*H)^{jk}, & G_{oi} = -\frac{1}{2}\eta_{oijk} (*G)^{jk}. \end{cases}$$

We deduce from (30-4), the following relations:

$$\begin{cases} e_i = -(*H)_{jk}, & d_i = -(*G)_{jk}, \\ b_i = H_{jk}, & h_i = G_{jk}, \end{cases} \tag{30-6}$$

where the permutation (i, j, k) of (1, 2, 3) is assumed even. Similarly, we have

$$\begin{cases} e^i = (*H)^{jk}, & d^i = (*G)^{jk}, \\ b^i = -H^{jk}, & h^i = -G^{jk}. \end{cases} \tag{30-7}$$

It is easy now to express the two tensors **H** and **G** in terms of the four vectors **e, d, b,** and **h.** In the rest frame $\{\mathbf{v}_{(\rho)}\}$ where $u^0 = 1$, $u^i = 0$, we can rewrite $H_{oi} = e_i$ as

$$H_{oi} = u_o e_i - u_i e_o - \eta_{oijk} u^j b^k,$$

and we can also rewrite $H_{jk} = -\eta_{jk\,oi} (*H)^{oi} = -\eta_{jkoi} b^i$ as

$$H_{jk} - u_j e_k - u_k e_j - \eta_{jk\lambda\mu} u^\lambda b^\mu.$$

We thus obtain the unique tensorial formula,

$$H_{\alpha\beta} = u_\alpha e_\beta - u_\beta e_\alpha - \eta_{\alpha\beta\lambda\mu} u^\lambda b^\mu, \tag{30-8}$$

which is true in an arbitrary frame. Similarly, we have

$$G_{\alpha\beta} = u_\alpha d_\beta - u_\beta d_\alpha - \eta_{\alpha\beta\lambda\mu} u^\lambda h^\mu . \tag{30-9}$$

We seek now the expressions for ***H** and for ***G**. In the rest frame $\{\mathbf{v}_{(\rho)}\}$, we can rewrite the relation $(*H)_{oi} = b_i$ as

$$(*H)_{oi} = u_o b_i - u_i b_o + \eta_{oijk} u^j e^k,$$

and we can also rewrite $(*H)_{jk} = \eta_{jkoi} H^{oi} = \eta_{jkoi} e^i$ as

$$(*H)_{jk} = u_j b_k - u_k b_j + \eta_{jk\lambda\mu} u^\lambda e^\mu .$$

We obtain the formulas,

$$(*H)_{\alpha\beta} = u_\alpha b_\beta - u_\beta b_\alpha + \eta_{\alpha\beta\lambda\mu} u^\lambda e^\mu \tag{30-10}$$

and

$$(*G)_{\alpha\beta} = u_\alpha h_\beta - u_\beta h_\alpha + \eta_{\alpha\beta\lambda\mu} u^\lambda d^\mu . \tag{30-11}$$

We can write (30-8) and (30-9) in terms of exterior products:

$$\mathbf{H} = \mathbf{u} \wedge \mathbf{e} - *(\mathbf{u} \wedge \mathbf{b}), \qquad \mathbf{G} = \mathbf{u} \wedge \mathbf{d} - *(\mathbf{u} \wedge \mathbf{h}) \tag{30-12}$$

and by the operation $*$, we obtain directly

$$*\mathbf{H} = \mathbf{u} \wedge \mathbf{b} + *(\mathbf{u} \wedge \mathbf{e}), \qquad *\mathbf{G} = \mathbf{u} \wedge \mathbf{h} + *(\mathbf{u} \wedge \mathbf{d}).$$

(**c**) In the theory of Maxwell, the inductions depend linearly on the fields and are given by *constitutive equations*; these equations depend on the nature of the matter. We consider here the *isotropic case*, and we write as constitutive equations,

$$\mathbf{d} = \lambda \mathbf{e}, \qquad \mathbf{b} = \mu \mathbf{h}. \tag{30-13}$$

Here λ is the *dielectric permitivity* of the matter, and μ the *magnetic permeability*.

From these relations, it is possible to deduce a simple

expression for $\mathbf{G}$ in terms of $\mathbf{H}$. According to (30-12) and (30-13), we have

$$\mathbf{G} = \lambda(\mathbf{u} \wedge \mathbf{e}) - \frac{1}{\mu} *(\mathbf{u} \wedge \mathbf{b}),$$

but,

$$-*(\mathbf{u} \wedge \mathbf{b}) = \mathbf{H} - \mathbf{u} \wedge \mathbf{e}.$$

It follows that

$$\mathbf{G} = \frac{1}{\mu} \mathbf{H} + \frac{\lambda\mu - 1}{\mu} \mathbf{u} \wedge \mathrm{e}, \tag{30-14}$$

or more explicitly

$$G_{\alpha\beta} = \frac{1}{\mu} H_{\alpha\beta} + \frac{\lambda\mu - 1}{\mu} (u_\alpha u^\rho H_{\rho\beta} - u_\beta u^\rho H_{\rho\alpha}). \tag{30-15}$$

31. Maxwell Equations and Energy Tensor of Minkowski

(a) We assume that, in the considered domain of V_4, the electromagnetic field satisfies Maxwell equations

$$d\mathbf{H} = 0 \qquad \text{or} \qquad \delta(*\mathbf{H}) = 0 \tag{31-1}$$

and

$$\delta\mathbf{G} = -\mathbf{J}, \tag{31-2}$$

where $\mathbf{J}$ is the electric current. According to $\delta^2 = 0$, we have

$$\delta\mathbf{J} = 0, \tag{31-3}$$

which is the equation of conservation of electricity. The

electric current is still the sum of two terms corresponding respectively to the convection current and to the conduction current.

$$J^{\beta} = \epsilon u^{\beta} + \sigma u_{\alpha} H^{\alpha\beta} = \epsilon u^{\beta} + \sigma e^{\beta}, \qquad (31\text{-}4)$$

where ϵ is the *proper density of electric charge* and σ the *conductivity* of the fluid (§19).

(**b**) Let us consider Minkowski's energy tensor, defined by [10]:

$$\tau_{\alpha\beta} = \tfrac{1}{4} g_{\alpha\beta} H_{\rho\sigma} G^{\rho\sigma} - H_{\alpha\beta} G_{\beta}{}^{\rho} . \qquad (31\text{-}5)$$

This tensor is not symmetrical in general. The nonsymmetry of Minkowski's tensor has given to a long discussion in the literature. But we will see that this tensor is symmetrical in the case of the relativistic magnetohydrodynamics and we can adopt this energy tensor here, without discussion.

We seek to express $\tau_{\alpha\beta}$ in terms of the four vectors **e**, **d**, **b**, **h**. According to (30-8) and (30-9), we have

$$H_{\alpha\rho} G_{\beta}{}^{\rho} = (u_{\alpha} e_{\rho} - u_{\rho} e_{\alpha} - \eta_{\alpha\rho\lambda\mu} u^{\lambda} b^{\mu})$$
$$\times (u_{\beta} d^{\rho} - u^{\rho} d_{\beta} - \eta_{\beta}{}^{\rho\nu\sigma} u_{\nu} h_{\sigma}) .$$

If we set

$$v_{\alpha} = \eta_{\alpha\rho\lambda\mu} e^{\rho} h^{\lambda} u^{\mu}, \qquad w_{\alpha} = \eta_{\alpha\rho\lambda\mu} d^{\rho} b^{\lambda} u^{\mu}, \qquad (31\text{-}6)$$

we obtain

$$H_{\alpha\rho} G_{\beta}{}^{\rho} = u_{\alpha} u_{\beta} e_{\rho} d^{\rho} + e_{\alpha} d_{\beta}$$
$$+ (u_{\alpha} v_{\beta} + u_{\beta} w_{\alpha}) + U_{\alpha\beta} .$$

$$U_\alpha^\beta = \eta_{\alpha\rho\lambda\mu}\,\eta^{\beta\rho\nu\sigma}\,u^\lambda\, b^\mu\, u_\nu\, h_\sigma$$

$$= -\epsilon^{\beta\nu\sigma}_{\alpha\lambda\mu}\, u^\lambda\, b^\mu\, u_\nu\, h_\sigma ;$$

here ϵ is the permutation tensor of Kronecker. For $\alpha = \beta$, we obtain the term,

$$-g_\alpha^\beta\, b^\mu\, h_\mu ;$$

for $\alpha = \nu$, we have

$$u_\alpha\, u^\beta\, b^\mu\, h_\mu ;$$

and for $\alpha = \sigma$, we have

$$h_\alpha\, b^\beta .$$

We may therefore simplify the expression for u_α^β to

$$U_\alpha^\beta = u_\alpha\, u^\beta\, h_\rho\, b^\rho + h_\alpha\, b^\beta - g_\alpha^\beta\, h_\rho\, b^\rho ,$$

and thus

$$H_{\alpha\rho}\, G_\beta{}^\rho = u_\alpha\, u_\beta\, (e_\rho\, d^\rho + h_\rho\, b^\rho) + (e_\alpha\, d_\beta + h_\alpha\, b_\beta) + (u_\alpha\, v_\beta + u_\beta\, w_\alpha) - g_{\alpha\beta}\, h_\rho\, b^\rho . \qquad (31\text{-}7)$$

By contraction, we have

$$\tfrac{1}{2}\, H_{\rho\sigma}\, G^{\rho\sigma} = e_\rho\, d^\rho + h_\rho\, b^\rho - 2h_\rho\, b^\rho$$

$$= e_\rho\, d^\rho - h_\rho\, b^\rho .$$

It follows for the energy tensor

$$\tau_{\alpha\beta} = \tfrac{1}{2} g_{\alpha\beta}(e_\rho d^\rho - h_\rho b^\rho) - u_\alpha u_\beta (e_\rho d^\rho + h_\rho b^\rho)$$

$$- (e_\alpha d_\beta + h_\alpha b_\beta) - (u_\alpha v_\beta + u_\beta w_\alpha)$$

$$+ g_{\alpha\beta} h_\rho b^\rho,$$

that is,

$$\tau_{\alpha\beta} = (\tfrac{1}{2} g_{\alpha\beta} - u_\alpha u_\beta)(e_\rho d^\rho + h_\rho b^\rho)$$

$$- (e_\alpha d_\beta + h_\alpha b_\beta) - (u_\alpha v_\beta + u_\beta w_\alpha). \qquad (31\text{-}8)$$

According to (30-13), we have $w_\alpha = \lambda\mu v_\alpha$, and thus

$$\tau_{\alpha\beta} = (\tfrac{1}{2} g_{\alpha\beta} - u_\alpha u_\beta)(e_\rho d^\rho + h_\rho b^\rho)$$

$$- (e_\alpha d_\beta + h_\alpha b_\beta) - (u_\alpha v_\beta + \lambda\mu u_\beta v_\alpha). \qquad (31\text{-}9)$$

If we introduce the rest frame $\{\mathbf{v}_{(\rho)}\}$, we see that the corresponding components of $\tau_{\alpha\beta}$ are

$$\tau_{00} = -\tfrac{1}{2}(e_\rho d^\rho + h_\rho b^\rho), \qquad \tau_{0i} = -v_i, \qquad \tau_{i0} = -w_i,$$

and

$$\tau_{ij} = \tfrac{1}{2} g_{ij}(e_\rho d^\rho + h_\rho b^\rho) - (e_i d_j + h_i b_j).$$

We thus obtain, respectively, the electromagnetic density, the Poynting vector corresponding to v^i, the momentum vector w^i proportional to the Poynting vector, and the Maxwell spatial stress tensor τ_{ij}.

(c) We seek to compute the force density given by

$$\nabla_\beta \tau_\alpha^\beta = -H_{\alpha\rho} \nabla_\beta G^{\beta\rho} - G^{\beta\rho} \nabla_\beta H_{\alpha\rho}$$

$$+ \tfrac{1}{4}(G^{\rho\sigma} \nabla_\alpha H_{\rho\sigma} + H_{\rho\sigma} \nabla_\alpha G^{\rho\sigma}). \qquad (31\text{-}10)$$

According to the Maxwell equations, we have

$$\nabla_\beta G^{\beta\rho} = J^\rho$$

and

$$G^{\beta\rho}(\nabla_\beta H_{\alpha\rho} + \nabla_\alpha H_{\rho\beta} + \nabla_\rho H_{\beta\alpha}) = 0,$$

which give

$$2G^{\beta\rho}\nabla_\beta H_{\alpha\rho} = G^{\beta\rho}\nabla_\alpha H_{\beta\rho}.$$

We thus obtain

$$\nabla_\beta \tau^\beta_\alpha = J^\rho H_{\rho\alpha} + \tfrac{1}{4}(H_{\rho\sigma}\nabla_\alpha G^{\rho\sigma} - G^{\rho\sigma}\nabla_\alpha H_{\rho\sigma}). \tag{31-11}$$

To transform the last term on the right-hand side, we use (30-15). It follows that

$$\begin{aligned}
&\tfrac{1}{2}(H_{\rho\sigma}\nabla_\alpha G^{\rho\sigma} - G^{\rho\sigma}\nabla_\alpha H_{\rho\sigma}) \\
&\quad = \tfrac{1}{2}\partial_\alpha\left(\frac{1}{\mu}\right)H_{\rho\sigma}H^{\rho\sigma} + \left\{\partial_\alpha\lambda - \partial_\alpha\left(\frac{1}{\mu}\right)\right\}e_\sigma e^\sigma \\
&\qquad + \frac{1}{2\mu}H_{\rho\sigma}\nabla_\alpha H^{\rho\sigma} + \frac{\lambda\mu - 1}{\mu}H_{\rho\sigma}\nabla_\alpha(u^\rho u^\tau H_\tau{}^\sigma) \\
&\qquad - \frac{1}{2\mu}H^{\rho\sigma}\nabla_\alpha H_{\rho\sigma} - \frac{\lambda\mu - 1}{\mu}\nabla_\alpha H_{\rho\sigma}u^\rho u^\tau H_\tau{}^\sigma,
\end{aligned}$$

or, after simplifications,

$$\begin{aligned}
&\tfrac{1}{2}(H_{\rho\sigma}\nabla_\alpha G^{\rho\sigma} - G^{\rho\sigma}\nabla_\alpha H_{\rho\sigma}) \\
&\quad = \partial_\alpha\left(\frac{1}{\mu}\right)(e_\sigma e^\sigma - b_\sigma b^\sigma) \\
&\qquad + \left\{\partial_\alpha\lambda - \partial_\alpha\left(\frac{1}{\mu}\right)\right\}e_\sigma e^\sigma \\
&\qquad + 2\frac{\lambda\mu - 1}{\mu}H_{\rho\sigma}H_\tau{}^\sigma\nabla_\alpha u^\rho u^\tau.
\end{aligned}$$

We obtain

$$\tfrac{1}{2}(H_{\rho\sigma}\nabla_\alpha G^{\rho\sigma} - G^{\rho\sigma}\nabla_\alpha H_{\rho\sigma})$$

$$= \partial_\alpha\lambda e_\sigma e^\sigma + \partial_\alpha\mu h_\sigma h^\sigma$$

$$+ 2\frac{\lambda\mu - 1}{\mu} H_{\rho\sigma} e^\sigma \nabla_\alpha u^\rho .$$

But, according to (30-8),

$$H_{\rho\sigma} e^\sigma = u_\rho (e_\sigma e^\sigma) - \eta_{\rho\sigma\lambda\mu} e^\sigma u^\lambda b^\mu$$

$$= (e_\sigma e^\sigma) u_\rho + \mu v_\rho .$$

We have, therefore,

$$\tfrac{1}{2}(H_{\rho\sigma}\nabla_\alpha G^{\rho\sigma} - G^{\rho\sigma}\nabla_\alpha H_{\rho\sigma})$$

$$= \partial_\alpha\lambda e_\sigma e^\sigma + \partial_\alpha\mu h_\sigma h^\sigma + 2(\lambda\mu - 1) v_\rho \nabla_\alpha u^\rho ,$$

that is,

$$\nabla_\beta \tau^\beta_\alpha = J^\rho H_{\rho\alpha} + \tfrac{1}{2}[\partial_\alpha\lambda(e_\sigma e^\sigma) + \partial_\alpha\mu(h_\sigma h^\sigma)]$$

$$+ (w_\rho - v_\rho)\nabla_\alpha u^\rho . \tag{31-12}$$

The second term of the right-hand side of (31-12) is null if λ and μ are constant. The last term appears in classical physics for a rotating body; it is zero if, for example, $v_\rho = 0$ or $\nabla_\alpha u^\rho = 0$.

It is interesting to evaluate the first term. We have

$$J^\rho H_{\rho\alpha} = (\epsilon u^\rho + \sigma e^\rho)(u_\rho e_\alpha - u_\alpha e_\rho - \eta_{\rho\alpha\lambda\mu} u^\lambda b^\mu).$$

It follows that

$$J^\rho H_{\rho\alpha} = \epsilon e_\alpha - \sigma(e^\rho e_\rho) u_\alpha - \sigma\eta_{\alpha\rho\lambda\mu} e^\rho b^\lambda u^\mu ,$$

that is,

$$J^{\rho} H_{\rho\alpha} = \epsilon e_{\alpha} - \sigma(e^{\rho} e_{\rho}) u_{\alpha} - \sigma \mu v_{\alpha}. \tag{31-13}$$

The different terms of the right-hand side of (31-13) have clear physical meanings.

32. The Case of the Magnetohydrodynamics [2, 13]

(**a**) Perfect magnetohydrodynamics is the study of the properties of a perfect fluid *with an infinite conductivity* $\sigma = \infty$. *The electric current* **J**, *and thus the product* σ**e** *being essentially finite, we have necessarily in this case* **e** = 0. The electromagnetic field is reduced to *a magnetic field* **h** *with respect to the velocity of the considered fluid.*

It follows from (30-15) and (30-10) that

$$G_{\alpha\beta} = \frac{1}{\mu} H_{\alpha\beta} \tag{32-1}$$

and

$$(*H)_{\alpha\beta} = \mu(u_{\alpha} h_{\beta} - u_{\beta} h_{\alpha}). \tag{32-2}$$

We assume for simplicity in the following part that *the magnetic permeability* μ *is a given constant.* This assumption μ = const. is not absolutely essential.

(**b**) According to (31-5), the part of the energy tensor corresponding to the field can be written

$$\tau_{\alpha\beta} = \mu(\tfrac{1}{4} g_{\alpha\beta} G_{\rho\sigma} G^{\rho\sigma} - G_{\alpha\rho} G_{\beta}{}^{\rho}). \tag{32-3}$$

This tensor is here *symmetrical.*

It follows from (31-9) that in this case, where $e_{\alpha} = 0$, $v_{\alpha} = 0$, we have for $\tau_{\alpha\beta}$ the following expression:

$$\tau_{\alpha\beta} = \mu[(\tfrac{1}{2} g_{\alpha\beta} - u_{\alpha} u_{\beta}) h_{\rho} h^{\rho} - h_{\alpha} h_{\beta}]. \tag{32-4}$$

The vector h_{ρ} being a space-like vector, we set in the following part:

$$|\mathbf{h}|^2 = -h_\rho h^\rho \geq 0, \tag{32-5}$$

and so we have for $\tau_{\alpha\beta}$ the convenient formula,

$$\tau_{\alpha\beta} = \mu[(u_\alpha u_\beta - \tfrac{1}{2}g_{\alpha\beta})|\mathbf{h}|^2 - h_\alpha h_\beta]. \tag{32-6}$$

(**c**) In the case of the magnetohydrodynamics, the electric current **J** is not known, but it is only defined by $-\delta\mathbf{G}$. The Maxwell equations are reduced to (31-1), that is, to

$$\nabla_\alpha(u^\alpha h^\beta - u^\beta h^\alpha) = 0. \tag{32-7}$$

We expand these equations,

$$h^\beta \nabla_\alpha u^\alpha + u^\alpha \nabla_\alpha h^\beta - h^\alpha \nabla_\alpha u^\beta - u^\beta \nabla_\alpha h^\alpha = 0, \tag{32-8}$$

and we form two interesting consequences of the Maxwell equations. According to $h^\beta u_\beta = 0$ and the unitary character of u_β, we obtain, by multiplying (32-8) by u_β,

$$u^\alpha u^\beta \nabla_\alpha h_\beta - \nabla_\alpha h^\alpha = 0. \tag{32-9}$$

Similarly, we obtain, by contracting the product of (32-8) with h_β,

$$h_\beta h^\beta \nabla_\alpha u^\alpha + u^\alpha h_\beta \nabla_\alpha h^\beta - h^\alpha h^\beta \nabla_\alpha u_\beta = 0,$$

that is, with $|\mathbf{h}|^2 = -h_\beta h^\beta$,

$$\tfrac{1}{2} u^\alpha \nabla_\alpha |\mathbf{h}|^2 + |\mathbf{h}|^2 \nabla_\alpha u^\alpha + h^\alpha h^\beta \nabla_\alpha u_\beta = 0. \tag{32-10}$$

It is possible to transform (32-10) into the equivalent form,

$$\tfrac{1}{2} u^\alpha \nabla_\alpha |\mathbf{h}|^2 + |\mathbf{h}|^2 \nabla_\alpha u^\alpha - h^\alpha u^\beta \nabla_\alpha h_\beta = 0. \tag{32-11}$$

33. The Main Equations of Relativistic Magnetohydrodynamics

(**a**) In the following part, we shall consider a relativistic thermodynamical perfect fluid with a magnetic permeability μ = constant and an infinite conductivity σ; the total energy tensor is here the sum of the dynamic energy tensor of the fluid and of the energy tensor of the electromagnetic field,

$$T_{\alpha\beta} = (rfu_\alpha u_\beta - \frac{p}{c^2} g_{\alpha\beta}) + \tau_{\alpha\beta}. \tag{33-1}$$

As in the previous cases (§9, §10, and §19), r is the *proper matter density* of the fluid, p its pressure, **u** the unitary velocity, and f the *index of the fluid* which is given by

$$f = 1 + \frac{i}{c^2},$$

where i is the specific enthalpy.

According to expression (32-6) for $\tau_{\alpha\beta}$, it is possible to write the energy tensor

$$T_{\alpha\beta} = (rf + p|\mathbf{h}|^2)u_\alpha u_\beta - \left(\frac{p}{c^2} + \frac{1}{2}\mu|\mathbf{h}|^2\right) g_{\alpha\beta} - \mu h_\alpha h_\beta. \tag{33-2}$$

From this we see that

$$T_{\alpha\beta} u^\beta = \left(rf + \tfrac{1}{2}\mu|\mathbf{h}|^2 - \frac{p}{c^2}\right) u^\alpha.$$

The proper energy density of our fluid is (compared to §9)

$$rf - \frac{p}{c^2} + \frac{1}{2}\mu|\mathbf{h}|^2 = \rho + \tfrac{1}{2}\mu|\mathbf{h}|^2,$$

where ρ is the dynamic part and $\frac{1}{2}\mu|\mathbf{h}|^2$ the magnetic part.

We can interpret the coefficient $(p/c^2 + \frac{1}{2}\mu|\mathbf{h}|^2)$ of $g_{\alpha\beta}$ in (33-2), saying that the magnetic field gives here a supplementary pressure equal to $\frac{1}{2}c^2\mu|\mathbf{h}|^2$.

(b) If T is the proper temperature of the fluid and S its specific entropy, we have

$$TdS = di - \frac{dp}{r}$$

and, thus,

$$dp = c^2 r df - r T dS. \tag{33-3}$$

We always consider r as a given function of the two thermodynamical variables f and S, depending on the internal structure of the fluid

$$r = r(f, S).$$

(c) The main equations of relativistic magnetohydrodynamics are the Einstein equations

$$S_{\alpha\beta} = \chi T_{\alpha\beta}, \tag{33-4}$$

where $T_{\alpha\beta}$ is given by (33-2), and the Maxwell equations

$$\nabla_\alpha (u^\alpha h^\beta - u^\beta h^\alpha) = 0. \tag{33-5}$$

We will add, in a moment, the assumption that r *is conservative* in the motion of the fluid.

34. The Equation of Continuity and the Differential System of the Stream Lines

(a) We consider now the equations of conservation $\nabla_\alpha T^\alpha_{\beta\cdot} = 0$, which are consequences of the Einstein equations (33-4). Since

$$T_{\alpha\beta} = (rf + \mu |\mathbf{h}|^2) u_\alpha u_\beta - \left(\frac{p}{c^2} + \tfrac{1}{2}\mu |\mathbf{h}|^2\right) g_{\alpha\beta} - \mu h_\alpha h_\beta,$$

we have

$$\nabla_\alpha T^\alpha_\beta \equiv \nabla_\alpha[(rf + \mu|\mathbf{h}|^2)u^\alpha]u_\beta$$
$$+ (rf + \mu|\mathbf{h}|^2)u^\alpha \nabla_\alpha u_\beta - \partial_\beta\left(\frac{p}{c^2} + \frac{1}{2}\mu|\mathbf{h}|^2\right)$$
$$- \mu\nabla_\alpha h^\alpha h_\beta - \mu h^\alpha \nabla_\alpha h_\beta = 0. \quad (34\text{-}1)$$

It follows by contracting with u^β that

$$u^\beta \nabla_\alpha T^\alpha_\beta \equiv \nabla_\alpha[(rf + \mu|\mathbf{h}|^2)u^\alpha]$$
$$- u^\alpha \partial_\alpha\left(\frac{p}{c^2} + \frac{1}{2}\mu|\mathbf{h}|^2\right) - \mu h^\alpha u^\beta \nabla_\alpha h_\beta = 0; \quad (34\text{-}2)$$

that is,

$$\nabla_\alpha(rfu^\alpha) - u^\alpha \partial_\alpha \frac{p}{c^2}$$
$$+ \mu\{|\mathbf{h}|^2 \nabla_\alpha u^\alpha + \tfrac{1}{2}u^\alpha \partial_\alpha|\mathbf{h}|^2 - h^\alpha u^\beta \nabla_\alpha h_\beta\} = 0. \quad (34\text{-}3)$$

Thus, according to (32-11), (34-3) can be written

$$\nabla_\alpha(rfu^\alpha) - u^\alpha \frac{\partial_\alpha p}{c^2} = 0. \quad (34\text{-}4)$$

We have obtained the same equation of continuity as in §11, i.e.,

$$f\nabla_\alpha(ru^\alpha) + \frac{1}{c^2} rTu^\alpha \partial_\alpha S = 0.$$

We assume as before that *the motion of the fluid is locally adiabatic,*

$$u^\alpha \partial_\alpha S = 0 \quad (34\text{-}5)$$

or, equivalently, that *the matter density is conservative,*

$$\nabla_\alpha (ru^\alpha) = 0. \qquad (34\text{-}6)$$

(**b**) Now, we use (34-2) to transform the equations (34-1). We obtain

$$(rf + \mu\,|\mathbf{h}|^2)u^\alpha \nabla_\alpha u^\beta - (g^{\alpha\beta} - u^\alpha u^\beta)\partial_\alpha\left(\frac{p}{c^2} + \tfrac{1}{2}\mu\,|\mathbf{h}|^2\right)$$
$$+ \mu h^\lambda u^\mu \nabla_\lambda h_\mu u^\beta - \mu \nabla_\alpha h^\alpha h^\beta - \mu h^\alpha \nabla_\alpha h^\beta = 0. \qquad (34\text{-}7)$$

According to (32-11), the equations (34-7) can be written

$$(rf + \mu\,|\mathbf{h}|^2)u^\alpha \nabla_\alpha u^\beta$$
$$-(g^{\alpha\beta} - u^\alpha u^\beta)\partial_\alpha\left(\frac{p}{c^2} + \tfrac{1}{2}\mu\,|\mathbf{h}|^2\right)$$
$$+ \tfrac{1}{2}\mu u^\alpha \nabla_\alpha |\mathbf{h}|^2 u^\beta + \mu\,|\mathbf{h}|^2 \nabla_\alpha u^\alpha u^\beta$$
$$- \mu \nabla_\alpha h^\alpha h^\beta - \mu h^\alpha \nabla_\alpha h^\beta = 0. \qquad (34\text{-}8)$$

It is possible to transform (34-8), according to (33-3), in

$$(rf + \mu\,|\mathbf{h}|^2)u^\alpha \nabla_\alpha u^\beta - (g^{\alpha\beta} - u^\alpha u^\beta)$$
$$\times\left(r\partial_\alpha f + \tfrac{1}{2}\mu\partial_\alpha |\mathbf{h}|^2 - \frac{rT}{c^2}\,\partial_\alpha S\right)$$
$$+ \tfrac{1}{2}\mu u^\alpha \nabla_\alpha |\mathbf{h}|^2 u^\beta + \mu\,|\mathbf{h}|^2 \nabla_\alpha u^\alpha u^\beta$$
$$- \mu \nabla_\alpha h^\alpha h^\beta - \mu h^\alpha \nabla_\alpha h^\beta = 0. \qquad (34\text{-}9)$$

Equation (34-9) is the differential system of the stream lines of the fluid.

(**c**) We form now a simple and interesting consequence

of these equations of motion. It follows from (34-7), by contracting with h_β, that

$$(rf + \mu|h|^2)u^\alpha \nabla_\alpha u^\beta h_\beta - h^\alpha \partial_\alpha \left(\frac{p}{c^2} + \tfrac{1}{2}\mu|\mathbf{h}|^2\right)$$

$$+ \mu|\mathbf{h}|^2 \nabla_\alpha h^\alpha - \mu h^\alpha h_\beta \nabla_\alpha h^\beta = 0,$$

that is, according to $u^\beta h_\beta = 0$,

$$rfu^\alpha \nabla_\alpha u^\beta h_\beta - h^\alpha \partial_\alpha \frac{p}{c^2}$$

$$+ \mu[-|\mathbf{h}|^2 u^\alpha u^\beta \nabla_\alpha h_\beta - \tfrac{1}{2} h^\alpha \nabla_\alpha |\mathbf{h}|^2$$

$$+ |\mathbf{h}|^2 \nabla_\alpha h^\alpha + \tfrac{1}{2} h^\alpha \nabla_\alpha |\mathbf{h}|^2] = 0.$$

According to (32-9), we obtain

$$rfu^\alpha \nabla_\alpha u^\beta h_\beta - h^\alpha \partial_\alpha \frac{p}{c^2} = 0. \tag{34-10}$$

This equation can also be written

$$rfu^\alpha u^\beta \nabla_\alpha h_\beta + h^\alpha \partial_\alpha \frac{p}{c^2} = 0, \tag{34-11}$$

or, according to (32-9),

$$rf\nabla_\alpha h^\alpha + h^\alpha \partial_\alpha \frac{p}{c^2} = 0. \tag{34-12}$$

It follows from (33-3) that (34-12) can be written

$$\nabla_\alpha h^\alpha = -\frac{h^\alpha}{f}\left(\partial_\alpha f - \frac{T}{c^2}\partial_\alpha S\right). \tag{34-13}$$

35. Chararacteristics of the Relativistic Magnetohydrodynamics

(**a**) We now study the Cauchy problem for the main system of relativistic magnetohydrodynamics, defined by the Einstein equations:

$$S_{\alpha\beta} = \chi T_{\alpha\beta} = \chi \left[(rf + \mu|\mathbf{h}|^2) u_\alpha u_\beta - \left(\frac{p}{c^2} + \frac{1}{2}\mu|\mathbf{h}|^2\right) g_{\alpha\beta} - \mu h_\alpha h_\beta \right], \tag{35-1}$$

with

$$g^{\alpha\beta} u_\alpha u_\beta = 1 \tag{35-2}$$

and

$$u_\alpha h^\alpha = 0, \tag{35-3}$$

by the equation

$$u^\alpha \partial_\alpha S = 0, \tag{35-4}$$

and by the Maxwell equations (32-8):

$$u^\alpha \nabla_\alpha h^\beta + h^\beta \nabla_\alpha u^\alpha - h^\alpha \nabla_\alpha u^\beta - u^\beta \nabla_\alpha h^\alpha = 0. \tag{35-5}$$

On the hypersurface Σ, with the local equation $x^0 = 0$, we give the values of the potentials $g_{\alpha\beta}$ and of their first derivatives, the values of the u_α defining a unitary vector and, for example, the values of the total (dynamic plus magnetic) pressure,

$$q = \frac{p}{c^2} + \frac{1}{2}\mu|\mathbf{h}|^2. \tag{35-6}$$

We assume that these data are such that $g_{\alpha\beta} v^\alpha v^\beta$ is normal hyperbolic, that Σ is not tangent to the elementary cones ($g^{00} \neq 0$) and is not tangent to **u** ($u^0 \neq 0$), that $F^\rho = 0$ on Σ.

We know that we can deduce from the data the values of the S^0_α on Σ. According to (35-1), we have

$$(rf + \mu|\mathbf{h}|^2)u^0 u_\alpha - \mu h^0 h_\alpha = \chi^{-1} S^0_\alpha + q g^0_\alpha, \qquad (35\text{-}7)$$

where the vector of the right member is known on Σ. This vector can be decomposed, in one and only one way, into the sum of a vector proportional to **u** and of a vector **v** which is orthogonal to **u**,

$$\chi^{-1} S^0_\alpha + q g^0_\alpha = a u_\alpha + v_\alpha, \qquad (35\text{-}8)$$

where

$$a = \chi^{-1} u^\alpha S^0_\alpha + q u^0,$$

$$v_\alpha = \chi^{-1} S^0_\rho (g^\rho_\alpha - u^\rho u_\alpha) + q(g^0_\alpha - u^0 u_\alpha).$$

We have, by comparison with (35-7),

$$rf + \mu|\mathbf{h}|^2 = \chi^{-1} \frac{u^\alpha S^0_\alpha}{u^0} + q \qquad (35\text{-}9)$$

and

$$h^0 h_\alpha = -\mu^{-1}\chi^{-1} S^0_\rho (g^\rho_\alpha - u^\rho u_\alpha)$$
$$- \mu^{-1} q(g^0_\alpha - u^0 u_\alpha). \qquad (35\text{-}10)$$

It follows from (35-10) that

$$(h^0)^2 = -\mu^{-1}\chi^{-1} S^0_\rho (g^{\rho 0} - u^\rho u^0) - \mu^{-1} q[g^{00} - (u^0)^2].$$

We know from this equation the values on Σ of h^0 if, for the given Cauchy data, the right-hand side is positive. According to (35-10), we obtain the values of the h_α which define a vector orthogonal to u_α. The scalar $|\mathbf{h}|^2$ being now known on Σ, we know the values on Σ of rf and p and, thus, the values of the thermodynamical variables, according to the equation of state. We can consider that we know the values of f and S, for example. We suppose that the data satisfy the Maxwell equation corresponding to $\beta = 0$.

(b) From (35-1), we deduce

$$T = rf - 4\frac{p}{c^2},$$

and so (35-1) is equivalent to

$$R_{\alpha\beta} = \chi\left[(rf + \mu|\mathbf{h}|^2)u_\alpha u_\beta - \frac{1}{2}\left(rf + \mu|\mathbf{h}|^2 - 2\frac{p}{c^2}\right)g_{\alpha\beta} - \mu h_\alpha h_\beta\right]. \tag{35-11}$$

According to the argument of § 4, we can substitute for the system (35-1), (35-2), (35-3), (35-4), and (35-5), the system that includes (35-4); the 10 equations

$$R^{(h)}_{\alpha\beta} = \chi\left[(rf + \mu|\mathbf{h}|^2)u_\alpha u_\beta - \frac{1}{2}\left(rf + \mu|\mathbf{h}|^2 - 2\frac{p}{c^2}\right)g_{\alpha\beta} - \mu h_\alpha h_\beta\right]; \tag{35-12}$$

the equation equivalent to the equation of continuity

$$\nabla_\alpha(ru^\alpha) = r\nabla_\alpha u^\alpha + u^\alpha \partial_\alpha r = 0; \tag{35-13}$$

the system of the stream lines, which is given, according to (34-9), by

$$(rf + \mu |\mathbf{h}|^2) u^\alpha \nabla_\alpha u^\beta - (g^{\alpha\beta} - u^\alpha u^\beta)$$

$$\times \left(r\partial_\alpha f + \tfrac{1}{2}\mu \partial_\alpha |\mathbf{h}|^2 - \frac{rT}{c^2} \partial_\alpha S \right)$$

$$+ \tfrac{1}{2}\mu u^\alpha \nabla_\alpha |\mathbf{h}|^2 u^\beta + \mu |\mathbf{h}|^2 \nabla_\alpha u^\alpha u^\beta$$

$$- \mu \nabla_\alpha h^\alpha h^\beta - \mu h^\alpha \nabla_\alpha h^\beta = 0; \qquad (35\text{-}14)$$

and the system of the Maxwell equations

$$u^\alpha \nabla_\alpha h^\beta + h^\beta \nabla_\alpha u^\alpha - h^\alpha \nabla_\alpha u^\beta - u^\beta \nabla_\alpha h^\alpha = 0. \qquad (35\text{-}15)$$

We note that, according to (35-14) and (32-11), and as a consequence of the Maxwell equations, u_β, which is initially unitary, remains unitary.

We will assume that the Cauchy data are given in terms of formal series in the local coordinates, and we will seek a formal series corresponding to these Cauchy data and also for solving the system (35-4), (35-12), (35-13), (35-14), and (35-15). g^{00} being different from zero, we deduce from (35-12) the values on Σ of the derivatives $\partial_{00} g_{\alpha\beta}$. The equation (35-4) gives for $u^0 \neq 0$ the value on Σ of $\partial_0 S$.

To obtain the values on Σ of $\partial_0 u^0$, $\partial_0 f$, and $\partial_0 h^0$, we consider the following four equations. First, the equation of continuity (35-13) can be written

$$r\partial_0 u^0 + u^0 r'_f \partial_0 f \simeq 0, \qquad (35\text{-}16)$$

where the symbol $\simeq 0$ is the equivalence relation, modulo terms having known values on Σ.

Next we consider the two equations (32-9) and (32-11), which are consequences of the Maxwell equations. These equations can be written

$$u^0 u^\beta \partial_0 h_\beta - \partial_0 h^0 \simeq 0$$

and

$$\tfrac{1}{2}\, u^0 \partial_0 |\mathbf{h}|^2 + |\mathbf{h}|^2 \partial_0 u^0 - h^0 u^\beta \partial_0 h_\beta \simeq 0.$$

We obtain by a linear combination

$$\tfrac{1}{2}\, (u^0)^2 \partial_0 |\mathbf{h}|^2 + |\mathbf{h}|^2 u^0 \partial_0 u^0 - h^0 \partial_0 h^0 \simeq 0. \qquad (35\text{-}17)$$

We introduce now the equation (35-14) corresponding to $\beta = 0$:

$$\begin{aligned}(rf + \mu |\mathbf{h}|^2) u^0 \partial_0 u^0 &- [g^{00} - (u^0)^2]\, r \partial_0 f \\ &- [g^{00} - (u^0)^2]\, \tfrac{1}{2}\, \mu \partial_0 |\mathbf{h}|^2 + \tfrac{1}{2}\, \mu (u^0)^2 \partial_0 |\mathbf{h}|^2 \\ &+ \mu |\mathbf{h}|^2 u^0 \partial_0 u^0 - 2\mu h^0 \partial_0 h^0 \simeq 0.\end{aligned}$$

This equation can be written

$$\begin{aligned} r f u^0 \partial_0 u^0 &- [g^{00} - (u^0)^2]\, r \partial_0 f - \tfrac{1}{2}\, \mu g^{00} \partial_0 |\mathbf{h}|^2 \\ &+ \tfrac{1}{2}\, \mu (u^0)^2 \partial_0 |\mathbf{h}|^2 + \mu |\mathbf{h}|^2 u^0 \partial_0 u^0 \\ &- 2\mu h^0 \partial_0 h^0 \simeq 0,\end{aligned}$$

that is, according to (35-17),

$$r f u^0 \partial_0 u^0 - [g^{00} - (u^0)^2]\, r \partial_0 f - \tfrac{1}{2}\, \mu g^{00} \partial_0 |\mathbf{h}|^2 \simeq 0. \qquad (35\text{-}18)$$

The last of the four equations is the equation (34-13), a consequence of the equations of motion. This equation can be written

$$f \partial_0 h^0 + h^0 \partial_0 f \simeq 0. \qquad (35\text{-}19)$$

We now eliminate $\partial_0 |\mathbf{h}|^2$ between (35-17) and (35-18). We obtain then the system:

$$[rf(u^0)^2 + \mu|\mathbf{h}|^2 g^{00}]u^0 \partial_0 u^0 - (u^0)^2[g^{00} - (u^0)^2]r\partial_0 f$$

$$- \mu g^{00} h^0 \partial_0 h^0 \simeq 0, \tag{35-20}$$

$$r\partial_0 u^0 + u^0 r'_f \partial_0 f \simeq 0, \tag{35-21}$$

$$h^0 \partial_0 f + f\partial_0 h^0 \simeq 0, \tag{35-22}$$

for the three unknowns $\partial_0 u^0$, $r\partial_0 f$, and $f\partial_0 h^0$. The determinant of this system is

$$H = \begin{vmatrix} [rf(u^0)^2 + \mu|\mathbf{h}|^2 g^{00}]u^0 & -(u^0)^2[g^{00} - (u^0)^2] & -\frac{\mu}{f} g^{00} h^0 \\ r & u^0 \dfrac{r'_f}{r} & 0 \\ 0 & \dfrac{h^0}{r} & 1 \end{vmatrix}$$

which yields on expansion

$$H = [rf(u^0)^2 + \mu|\mathbf{h}|^2 g^{00}](u^0)^2 \frac{r'_f}{r}$$

$$+ r(u^0)^2[g^{00} - (u^0)^2] - \frac{\mu}{f} g^{00}(h^0)^2,$$

that is,

$$H = (fr'_j - r)(u^0)^4 + \left(r + \mu|\mathbf{h}|^2 \frac{r'_f}{r}\right) g^{00}(u^0)^2$$

$$- \frac{\mu}{f} g^{00}(h^0)^2. \tag{35-23}$$

If $H \neq 0$, we obtain thus the values on Σ of $\partial_0 u^0$, $\partial_0 f$, $\partial_0 h^0$ and, according to (35-18), the value of $\partial_0|\mathbf{h}|^2$.

(**c**) We seek now the values on Σ of $\partial_0 u^i$ and $\partial_0 h^i$. The Maxwell equations give for $\beta = i$

$$h^0 \partial_0 u^i - u^0 \partial_0 h^i \simeq 0 \tag{35-24}$$

and we deduce from the system of the stream lines for $\beta = i$,

$$(rf + \mu\,|\mathbf{h}|^2)u^0\partial_0 u^i - \mu h^0 \partial_0 h^i \simeq 0. \qquad (35\text{-}25)$$

The determinant K of the systems (35-24) and (35-25) for the unknowns $\partial_0 u^i$ and $\partial_0 h^i$ is equal to

$$K = (rf + \mu\,|\mathbf{h}|^2)(u^0)^2 - \mu(h^0)^2. \qquad (35\text{-}26)$$

If $K \neq 0$, we obtain the values on Σ of $\partial_0 u^i$ and $\partial_0 h^i$. There is compatibility with the value of $\partial_0|\mathbf{h}|^2$, since (35-18) is a consequence of the equations of motion.

Thus, under our assumptions $g^{00} \neq 0$, $u^0 \neq 0$, $H \neq 0$, $K \neq 0$, we have obtained the values on Σ of $\partial_0 u^\alpha$, $\partial_0 h^\alpha$, $\partial_0 f$, $\partial_0 S$ and the same conclusions are available for the determination of the succeeding derivatives: it is sufficient to derive in x^0 the different considered equations. We see that under these assumptions the formal series we sought is determined in a unique way. *If the data are analytic, we obtain thus one and only one analytic solution of the Cauchy problem corresponding to the system (35-4), (35-12), (35-13), (35-14), and (35-15).*

(d) We have now determined the characteristic manifolds of the previous system, that is the characteristics of relativistic magnetohydrodynamics. We find again the gravitational waves and the hypersurfaces generated by the stream lines. But, we have two other types of characteristic hypersurfaces. If $\varphi = 0$ is the local equation of a regular hypersurface, we have found:

1. *The hydrodynamical waves*, solutions of

$$P^{\lambda\mu\nu\rho}\partial_\lambda\varphi\,\partial_\mu\varphi\,\partial_\nu\varphi\,\partial_\rho\varphi = 0, \qquad (35\text{-}27)$$

where

$$P^{\lambda\mu\nu\rho} = (fr'_f - r)u^\lambda u^\mu u^\nu u^\rho + \left(r + \mu\,|\mathbf{h}|^2\,\frac{r'_f}{r}\right) g^{(\lambda\mu}u^\nu u^{\rho)} - \frac{\mu}{f}\, g^{(\lambda\rho}h^\nu h^{\rho)}. \qquad (35\text{-}28)$$

Here, (...) is the symbol of symmetrization. We note that we obtain in (35-27) an equation of degree 4 in $d\varphi$.

2. The so-called *Alfven waves*, solutions of

$$Q^{\lambda\mu}\partial_\lambda\varphi\partial_\mu\varphi = 0, \tag{35-29}$$

where

$$Q^{\lambda\mu} = (rf + \mu|\mathbf{h}|^2)u^\lambda u^\mu - \mu h^\lambda h^\mu. \tag{35-30}$$

We will study next these two types of waves.

36. Waves and Velocities of Propagation

(**a**) Let us consider a family of waves, with characteristic hypersurfaces Σ, with the local equation φ = constant. We decompose first the vector $\partial_\alpha\varphi$ into the sum of a vector proportional to **u** and of a vector **w** orthogonal to **u**,

$$\partial_\alpha\varphi = au_\alpha + w_\alpha, \tag{36-1}$$

where

$$a = u^\rho\partial_\rho\varphi, \qquad w_\alpha = \partial_\alpha\varphi - au_\alpha.$$

We set

$$|\mathbf{w}|^2 = -w_\alpha w^\alpha = -(\partial_\alpha\varphi - au_\alpha)(\partial^\alpha\varphi - au^\alpha),$$

and so obtain

$$|\mathbf{w}|^2 = -g^{\lambda\mu}\partial_\lambda\varphi\partial_\mu\varphi - a^2 + 2a^2,$$

that is,

$$|\mathbf{w}|^2 = -(g^{\lambda\mu} - u^\lambda u^\mu)\partial_\lambda\varphi\partial_\mu\varphi.$$

We introduce, in the following part, the negative quadratic form having for its coefficients:

$$\gamma^{\lambda\mu} = g^{\lambda\mu} - u^{\lambda} u^{\mu} \tag{36-2}$$

and thus

$$|\mathbf{w}|^2 = -\gamma^{\lambda\mu} \partial_\lambda \varphi \partial_\mu \varphi \geq 0. \tag{36-3}$$

According to (36-1), the vector $\mathbf{w}$ gives the *spatial direction of propagation of the waves,* with respect to $\mathbf{u}$. The corresponding normalized vector $\mathbf{t}$ is given by

$$w_\alpha = |\mathbf{w}| t_\alpha .$$

The *wave velocity* v is given by the coefficient of t^α in the

$$k^\alpha = u^\alpha - \frac{v}{c} t^\alpha,$$

such that

$$k^\alpha \partial_\alpha \varphi = 0.$$

According to (36-1), we obtain

$$(a u_\alpha + |\mathbf{w}| t_\alpha) \left(u^\alpha - \frac{v}{c} t^\alpha\right) = 0,$$

that is,

$$a - |\mathbf{w}| \frac{v}{c} = 0.$$

We thus have

$$\frac{v}{c} = \frac{a}{|\mathbf{w}|}$$

and we find again the formula (13-5):

$$\frac{v^2}{c^2} = -\frac{(u^\rho \partial_\rho \varphi)^2}{\gamma^{\lambda\mu} \partial_\lambda \varphi \partial_\mu \varphi}. \tag{36-4}$$

It follows that

$$1 - \frac{v^2}{c^2} = \frac{g^{\lambda\mu}\partial_\lambda \varphi \partial_\mu \varphi}{\gamma^{\lambda\mu}\partial_\lambda \varphi\partial_\mu \varphi}.$$

We have $v^2 \leq c^2$ if and only if the waves are either *time-like or tangent to the elementary cones.*

We introduce systematically, in the following part, *the component* h_n *of the magnetic field in the spatial direction of propagation of the waves*; let

$$h_n = h^\rho t_\rho = \frac{h^\rho w_\rho}{|\mathbf{w}|} = \frac{h^\rho \partial_\rho \varphi}{|\mathbf{w}|}, \tag{36-5}$$

we have then

$$h_n^2 = -\frac{(h^\rho \partial_\rho \varphi)^2}{\gamma^{\lambda\mu}\partial_\lambda \varphi\partial_\mu \varphi}. \tag{36-6}$$

(b) We consider now the hydrodynamical waves defined, according to (35-27), by

$$(fr_f' - r)(u^\lambda \partial_\lambda \varphi)^4 + \left(r + \mu|\mathbf{h}|^2 \frac{r_f'}{r}\right)(g^{\lambda\mu}\partial_\lambda \varphi \partial_\mu \varphi)$$
$$\times (u^\rho \partial_\rho \varphi)^2 - \frac{\mu}{f}(g^{\lambda\rho}\partial_\lambda \varphi \partial_\rho \varphi)(h^\rho \partial_\rho \varphi)^2 = 0, \tag{36-7}$$

which can be written, according to the definition of $\gamma^{\lambda\mu}$,

$$(fr_f' - r)(u^\rho \partial_\rho \varphi)^4 + \left(r + \mu|\mathbf{h}|^2 \frac{r_f'}{r}\right)(u^\rho \partial_\rho \varphi)^2$$
$$\times (\gamma^{\lambda\mu} + u^\lambda u^\mu)\partial_\lambda \varphi \partial_\mu \varphi - \frac{\mu}{f}(h^\rho \partial_\rho \varphi)^2$$
$$\times (\gamma^{\lambda\mu} + u^\lambda u^\mu)\partial_\lambda \varphi \partial_\mu \varphi = 0,$$

that is, according to the expression (36-6) for h_n^2,

$$\left(f^2 r_f' + \mu |\mathbf{h}|^2 \frac{f r_f'}{r}\right)(u^\rho \partial_\rho \varphi)^4 + \left(rf + \mu |\mathbf{h}|^2 \frac{f r_f'}{r} + \mu h_n^2\right)$$

$$\times (u^\rho \partial_\rho \varphi)^2 (\gamma^{\lambda\mu} \partial_\lambda \varphi \partial_\mu \varphi)$$

$$+ \mu h_n^2 (\gamma^{\lambda\mu} \partial_\lambda \varphi \partial_\mu \varphi)^2 = 0.$$

If v_H is a velocity wave given by (36-4), v_H is a zero of the equation obtained by division of the previous equation by $(\gamma^{\lambda\mu} \partial_\lambda \varphi \partial_\mu \varphi)^2$:

$$\left(f^2 r_f' + \mu |\mathbf{h}|^2 \frac{f r_f'}{r}\right)\left(\frac{v_H^2}{c^2}\right)^2$$

$$- \left(rf + \mu |\mathbf{h}|^2 \frac{f r_f'}{r} + \mu h_n^2\right)\frac{v_H^2}{c^2} + \mu h_n^2 = 0. \quad (36\text{-}8)$$

We will study this equation in a moment.

We consider now the Alfven waves given by

$$(rf + \mu |\mathbf{h}|^2)(u^\rho \partial_\rho \varphi)^2 - \mu (h^\rho \partial_\rho \varphi)^2 = 0. \quad (36\text{-}9)$$

According to the expression for h_n^2, we have

$$(rf + \mu |\mathbf{h}|^2)(u^\rho \partial_\rho \varphi)^2 + \mu h_n^2 (\gamma^{\lambda\mu} \partial_\lambda \varphi \partial_\mu \varphi) = 0.$$

If v_A is the corresponding velocity wave, v_A is solution of the equation,

$$(rf + \mu |\mathbf{h}|^2)\frac{v_A^2}{c^2} - \mu h_n^2 = 0. \quad (36\text{-}10)$$

(c) We will discuss now the existence and the magnitude of these different waves' velocities. We have, first, the following lemma.

Lemma. For the magnetic field, we have

$$h_n^2 \leq |\mathbf{h}|^2. \quad (36\text{-}11)$$

Indeed, in an orthonormalized rest frame $\{\mathbf{v}_{(\rho)}\}$, $(\mathbf{v}_{(0)} = \mathbf{u})$, we have

$$h^i \partial_i \varphi = g^{ij} h_i \partial_j \varphi$$

and, according to the Schwarz inequality,

$$(h^i \partial_i \varphi)^2 \leq (-g^{ij} h_i h_j)(-g^{ij} \partial_i \varphi \partial_j \varphi),$$

that is,

$$(h^\alpha \partial_\alpha \varphi)^2 \leq |\mathbf{h}|^2 (-\gamma^{\lambda\mu} \partial_\lambda \varphi \partial_\mu \varphi)$$

or

$$h_n^2 \leq |\mathbf{h}|^2.$$

We have the equality in (36-11) if and only if $\mathbf{h}$ *is proportional to the spatial vector* $\mathbf{t}$ of propagation of the waves.

We now set

$$\gamma = \frac{fr'_j}{r} = \frac{c^2}{v_0^2}, \tag{36-12}$$

where v_0 is the velocity of the hydrodynamic waves, when the magnetic field is zero. We assume, in the following part,

$$\gamma \geq 1,$$

that is, $v_0 \leq c$, and we set

$$F(x) = (rf + \mu |\mathbf{h}|^2)\gamma x^2$$
$$- (rf + \mu |\mathbf{h}|^2 \gamma + \mu h_n^2)x + \mu h_n^2. \tag{36-13}$$

The relation (36-8) can be written

$$F\left(\frac{v_H^2}{c^2}\right) = 0.$$

For $F(x)$, we have the following values:

$$F(0) = \mu h_n^2 \geq 0, \qquad F(1) = rf(\gamma - 1) \geq 0.$$

But, if we consider

$$F\left(\frac{v_0^2}{c^2}\right) = F\left(\frac{1}{\gamma}\right) = (rf + \mu|\mathbf{h}|^2)\frac{1}{\gamma}$$
$$- (rf + \mu|\mathbf{h}|^2\gamma + \mu h_n^2)\frac{1}{\gamma} + \mu h_n^2,$$

we have

$$F\left(\frac{v_0^2}{c^2}\right) = \mu(|\mathbf{h}|^2 - h_n^2)\left(\frac{1}{\gamma} - 1\right) \leq 0.$$

We see that $F(x) = 0$ has two solutions between 0 and 1. It follows that there exists, for the hydrodynamic waves, two velocities v_{H_1} and v_{H_2}, such that

$$v_{H_1} \leq v_0 \leq v_{H_2} \leq c. \tag{36-14}$$

v_{H_1} is called the velocity of the *slow hydrodynamic waves* and v_{H_2} the velocity of the *fast hydrodynamic waves*.

If v_A is the velocity of the Alfven waves, we have, according to (36-10),

$$\frac{v_A^2}{c^2} = \frac{\mu h_n^2}{rf + \mu|\mathbf{h}|^2}.$$

According to the lemma, it is clear that

$$\mu h_n^2 \leq rf + \mu|\mathbf{h}|^2,$$

that is, $v_A \leq c$.

We consider now

$$F\left(\frac{v_A^2}{c^2}\right) = F\left(\frac{\mu h_n^2}{rf + \mu|\mathbf{h}|^2}\right)$$

$$= \frac{\mu h_n^2}{rf + \mu|\mathbf{h}|^2}[\mu h_n^2\gamma - (rf + \mu|\mathbf{h}|^2\gamma + \mu h_n^2)$$

$$+ rf + \mu|\mathbf{h}|^2].$$

We have

$$F\left(\frac{v_A^2}{c^2}\right) = \frac{\mu h_n^2}{rf + \mu|\mathbf{h}|^2}$$

$$\times\ \mu(h_n^2 - |\mathbf{h}|^2)(\gamma - 1) \leq 0. \qquad (36\text{-}15)$$

It follows that we have the inequalities,

$$v_{H_1} \leq v_A \leq v_{H_2}. \qquad (36\text{-}16)$$

(**d**) *We now assume that*

$$\gamma > 1$$

and we consider simple special cases.

We assume first that φ = constant *are Alfven waves and that* **h** *is along the spatial direction of propagation of the waves, that is* $h_n^2 = |\mathbf{h}|^2$. It follows from (36-13) that

$$F\left(\frac{v_A^2}{c^2}\right) = 0.$$

We see that our waves are also hydrodynamical waves. We have also

$$F\left(\frac{v_0^2}{c^2}\right) = 0,$$

and, in this case, v_{H_1} and v_{H_2} are respectively equal to the smaller and the greater of v_0 and v_A.

Now, *if* φ = constant *are hydrodynamical waves and if* h *is orthogonal to the spatial direction of propagation of the waves* ($h_n = 0$), *we have*

$$F(x) = (rf + \mu|\mathbf{h}|^2)\gamma x^2 - (rf + \mu|\mathbf{h}|^2\gamma)x.$$

We see that $v_{H_1} = 0$ and that

$$\frac{v_{H_2}^2}{c^2} = \frac{rf + \mu|\mathbf{h}|^2\gamma}{(rf + \mu|\mathbf{h}|^2)\gamma}$$

$$= \frac{rf + \mu|\mathbf{h}|^2 + \mu|\mathbf{h}|^2(\gamma - 1)}{(rf + \mu|\mathbf{h}|^2)\gamma}$$

$$= \frac{1}{\gamma} + \frac{\mu|\mathbf{h}|^2}{rf + \mu|\mathbf{h}|^2}\,\frac{\gamma - 1}{\gamma},$$

that is,

$$\frac{v_{H_2}^2}{c^2} = \frac{v_0^2}{c^2} + \frac{\mu|\mathbf{h}|^2}{rf + \mu|\mathbf{h}|^2}\left(1 - \frac{v_0^2}{c^2}\right). \qquad (36\text{-}17)$$

In this case, only one velocity exists [13].

37. Some Formulas with a Physical Interest

(a) Let **H** be the electromagnetic field tensor; H is closed (d**H** = 0) and, according to (30-8), we have

$$\mathbf{H} = -\mu[*(\mathbf{u} \wedge \mathbf{h})].$$

Thus, if **u** is the velocity vector of the fluid and **h** the magnetic field

$$i(\mathbf{u})\mathbf{H} = 0, \qquad i(\mathbf{h})\mathbf{H} = 0. \qquad (37\text{-}1)$$

According to the expression for the Lie derivative of a form, we have

$$\mathcal{L}(\mathbf{u})\mathbf{H} = 0, \tag{37-2}$$

and similarly

$$\mathcal{L}(\mathbf{h})\mathbf{H} = 0. \tag{37-3}$$

We see in (37-2) that **H** *is invariant by the system of the stream lines*. If D is a 2-dimensional domain of the fluid, the integral

$$\int_D \mathbf{H}$$

is invariant by an arbitrary deformation of D along the stream lines. We obtain thus the important result that **H** *defines an absolute invariant integral for the system of the stream lines.*

Let ψ be the local vector potential such that $\mathbf{H} = d\psi$. If C is the 1-dimensional boundary of a sufficiently small domain D, we have, according to the Stokes formula, for convenient orientations,

$$\begin{aligned} \int_C \psi &= \int_{\partial D} \psi \\ &= \int_D d\psi \\ &= \int_D \mathbf{H}. \end{aligned}$$

Thus, the integral $\int_C \psi$ is also invariant by an arbitrary deformation of C along the stream lines; ψ defines a relative invariant integral for the system of the stream lines.

Similar results are available for the magnetic lines, trajectories of **h**.

(**b**) Let us consider now the Maxwell equations $d\mathbf{H} = 0$, in the form (32-8),

$$u^\alpha \nabla_\alpha h^\beta + h^\beta \nabla_\alpha u^\alpha = h^\alpha \nabla_\alpha u^\beta + u^\beta \nabla_\alpha h^\alpha. \tag{37-4}$$

According to the equations of continuity $\nabla_\alpha(ru^\alpha) = 0$, we have

$$\nabla_\alpha u^\alpha = -u^\alpha \frac{\partial_\alpha r}{r}$$

and so (37-4) can be written

$$u^\alpha\left(\frac{\nabla_\alpha h^\beta}{r} - \frac{\partial_\alpha r}{r^2}\,h^\beta\right) = \frac{h^\alpha}{r}\nabla_\alpha u^\beta + \frac{u^\beta}{r}\nabla_\alpha h^\alpha.$$

Thus, the Maxwell equations are here equivalent to

$$u^\alpha \nabla_\alpha\left(\frac{h^\beta}{r}\right) = \frac{h^\alpha}{r}\nabla_\alpha u^\beta + u^\beta\frac{\nabla_\alpha h^\alpha}{r} \tag{37-5}$$

modulo the equation of continuity.

If we multiply (37-5) by $2h_\beta/r$, we obtain

$$2u^\alpha \frac{h_\beta}{r}\nabla_\alpha\left(\frac{h^\beta}{r}\right) = 2\,\frac{h^\alpha h^\beta}{r^2}\nabla_\alpha u_\beta,$$

that is,

$$u^\alpha \nabla_\alpha\left(\frac{|\mathbf{h}|^2}{r^2}\right) = -\frac{h^\alpha h^\beta}{r^2}(\nabla_\alpha u_\beta + \nabla_\beta u_\alpha). \tag{37-6}$$

Equations (37-5) and (37-6) are relativistic extensions of well-known formulas of classical magnetohydrodynamics. It is also easy to deduce (37-6) from the formula (32-10) and from the equation of continuity.

38. The Case of an Incompressible Fluid

(**a**) Let us consider the case *where our fluid is incompressible,* that is, according to §17, the case where *we have* $v_0 = c$ *or* $\gamma = 1$.

If φ = const. are *Alfven waves,* we have still, according to (36-15),

$$F\left(\frac{v_A^2}{c^2}\right) = 0,$$

and so we see that the Alfven waves are also hydrodynamical waves. Moreover,

$$F(1) = 0.$$

It follows that, in this case, we have

$$v_{H_1} = v_A, \qquad v_{H_2} = v_0 = c. \tag{38-1}$$

(b) We have seen, in §17, that for an incompressible fluid the equation of continuity $\nabla_\alpha(ru^\alpha) = 0$ implies

$$\nabla_\alpha(fu^\alpha) = 0.$$

We introduce now the *total index* k of the fluid in the presence of a magnetic field, defined by

$$k = \frac{rf + \mu|h|^2}{r} = f + \mu\frac{|h|^2}{r}, \tag{38-2}$$

and we consider the corresponding current

$$\Gamma^\alpha = ku^\alpha. \tag{38-3}$$

We have for an incompressible fluid

$$\nabla_\alpha\Gamma^\alpha = \nabla_\alpha\left[\left(f + \mu\frac{|\mathbf{h}|^2}{r}\right)u^\alpha\right] = \mu\nabla_\alpha\left(\frac{|\mathbf{h}|^2}{r^2}ru^\alpha\right),$$

that is,

$$\nabla_\alpha\Gamma^\alpha = \mu\frac{|\mathbf{h}|^2}{r^2}\nabla_\alpha(ru^\alpha) + \mu ru^\alpha\nabla_\alpha\left(\frac{|\mathbf{h}|^2}{r^2}\right).$$

We deduce from the formula (37-6),

$$\nabla_\alpha \Gamma^\alpha = -\mu \frac{h^\alpha h^\beta}{r} (\nabla_\alpha u_\beta + \nabla_\beta u_\alpha)$$

or

$$\delta\Gamma = \mu \frac{h^\alpha h^\beta}{r} (\nabla_\alpha u_\beta + \nabla_\beta u_\alpha). \tag{38-4}$$

39. Equations of the Helmholtz Type

(a) We introduce systematically the total index

$$k = f + \mu \frac{|\mathbf{h}|^2}{r}$$

and the corresponding current $\Gamma = k\mathbf{u}$ for the fluid. We choose here, as vorticity tensor,

$$\Pi = d\Gamma.$$

Equations of the Helmholtz type are equations giving the variation of the vorticity tensor Π along the current lines.

(b) First, I will transform the differential system of the stream lines, which can be written, according to (34-9) and $u^\alpha \partial_\alpha S = 0$,

$$rku^\alpha \nabla_\alpha u_\beta - (g_\beta^\alpha - u^\alpha u_\beta)\left(r\partial_\alpha f + \frac{\mu}{2} \partial_\alpha |\mathbf{h}|^2\right)$$

$$+ \frac{rT}{c^2} \partial_\beta S + \frac{\mu}{2} u^\alpha \partial_\alpha |\mathbf{h}|^2 u_\beta + \mu |\mathbf{h}|^2 \nabla_\alpha u^\alpha u_\beta$$

$$- \mu \nabla_\alpha (h^\alpha h_\beta) = 0. \tag{39-1}$$

We have, from the definition of the total index,

$$\partial_\alpha k = \partial_\alpha f + \frac{\mu}{r} \partial_\alpha |\mathbf{h}|^2 - \frac{\mu}{r^2} |\mathbf{h}|^2 \partial_\alpha r.$$

On substituting, we obtain for (39-1),

$$
\begin{aligned}
&ku^{\alpha}\nabla_{\alpha}u_{\beta} - (g^{\alpha}_{\beta} - u^{\alpha}u_{\beta}) \\
&\quad \times \left(\partial_{\alpha}k - \frac{\mu}{2r}\partial_{\alpha}|\mathbf{h}|^2 + \mu\frac{|\mathbf{h}|^2}{r^2}\partial_{\alpha}r\right) + \frac{T}{c^2}\partial_{\beta}S \\
&\quad + \frac{\mu}{2r}u^{\alpha}\partial_{\alpha}|\mathbf{h}|^2 u_{\beta} + \frac{\mu}{r}|\mathbf{h}|^2\nabla_{\alpha}u^{\alpha}u_{\beta} \\
&\quad - \frac{\mu}{r}\nabla_{\alpha}(h^{\alpha}h_{\beta}) = 0,
\end{aligned}
$$

that is,

$$
\begin{aligned}
&ku^{\alpha}\nabla_{\alpha}u_{\beta} - (g^{\alpha}_{\beta} - u^{\alpha}u_{\beta})\partial_{\alpha}k + \frac{\mu}{2r}\partial_{\beta}|\mathbf{h}|^2 \\
&\quad - \frac{\mu}{r^2}|\mathbf{h}|^2\partial_{\beta}r + \frac{T}{c^2}\partial_{\beta}S + \mu\frac{|\mathbf{h}|^2}{r^2} \\
&\quad \times (u^{\alpha}\partial_{\alpha}r + r\nabla_{\alpha}u^{\alpha})u_{\beta} - \frac{\mu}{r}\nabla_{\alpha}(h^{\alpha}h_{\beta}) = 0.
\end{aligned}
$$

According to the equation of continuity, it follows that

$$
\begin{aligned}
&ku^{\alpha}\nabla_{\alpha}u_{\beta} - (g^{\alpha}_{\beta} - u^{\alpha}u_{\beta})\partial_{\alpha}k + \frac{T}{c^2}\partial_{\beta}S \\
&\quad + \frac{\mu r}{2}\left(\frac{\partial_{\beta}|\mathbf{h}|^2}{r^2} - \frac{2|\mathbf{h}|^2}{r^3}\partial_{\beta}r\right) \\
&\quad - \frac{\mu}{r}\nabla_{\alpha}(h^{\alpha}h_{\beta}) = 0,
\end{aligned}
$$

that is,

$$
\begin{aligned}
&ku^{\alpha}\nabla_{\alpha}u_{\beta} - (g^{\alpha}_{\beta} - u^{\alpha}u_{\beta})\partial_{\alpha}k + \frac{T}{c^2}\partial_{\beta}S \\
&\quad + \frac{\mu r}{2}\partial_{\beta}\left(\frac{|\mathbf{h}|^2}{r^2}\right) - \frac{\mu}{r}\nabla_{\alpha}(h^{\alpha}h_{\beta}) = 0.
\end{aligned}
$$

It follows from the calculations of §12 that

$$u^{\alpha}\Pi_{\alpha\beta} = ku^{\alpha}\nabla_{\alpha}u_{\beta} - (g^{\alpha}_{\beta} - u^{\alpha}u_{\beta})\partial_{\alpha}k,$$

and so our equations of motion can be written

$$u^{\alpha}\Pi_{\alpha\beta} + \frac{T}{c^{1}}\partial_{\beta}S + \frac{\mu r}{2}\partial_{\beta}\left(\frac{|\mathbf{h}|^{2}}{r^{2}}\right)$$

$$- \frac{\mu}{r}(\nabla_{\alpha}h^{\alpha}h_{\beta} + h^{\alpha}\nabla_{\alpha}h_{\beta}) = 0. \qquad (39\text{-}2)$$

For the 1-form **h**, we have

$$h^{\alpha}\nabla_{\alpha}h_{\beta} = \mathcal{L}(\mathbf{h})h_{\beta} - \nabla_{\beta}h^{\alpha}h_{\alpha}$$

$$= \mathcal{L}(\mathbf{h})h_{\beta} + \tfrac{1}{2}\partial_{\beta}|\mathbf{h}|^{2}.$$

The equations (39-2) can be written without indices,

$$i(u)\Pi + \frac{T}{c^{2}}dS + \frac{\mu r}{2}d\left(\frac{|\mathbf{h}|^{2}}{r^{2}}\right)$$

$$+ \frac{\mu}{r}(\delta\mathbf{h}:\mathbf{h} - \mathcal{L}(\mathbf{h})\mathbf{h} - \tfrac{1}{2}d|\mathbf{h}|^{2}) = 0. \qquad (39\text{-}3)$$

(**b**) If we multiply (39-3) by k, we obtain

$$i(\Gamma)\Omega + \frac{Tk}{c^{2}}dS + \frac{\mu rk}{2}d\left(\frac{|\mathbf{h}|^{2}}{r^{2}}\right)$$

$$+ \frac{\mu k}{r}(\delta\mathbf{h}\cdot\mathbf{h} - \mathcal{L}(\mathbf{h})\mathbf{h} - \tfrac{1}{2}d|\mathbf{h}|^{2}) = 0.$$

The Lie derivative of the vorticity tensor Π with respect to Γ is then given by

$$\mathcal{L}(\Gamma)\Pi + \frac{1}{c^2} d(Tk) \wedge dS + \frac{\mu}{2} d(rk) \wedge d\left(\frac{|\mathbf{h}|^2}{r^2}\right)$$

$$+ \mu d\left(\frac{k}{r}\right) \wedge (\delta\mathbf{h}\cdot\mathbf{h} - \mathcal{L}(\mathbf{h})\mathbf{h} - \tfrac{1}{2} d|\mathbf{h}|^2)$$

$$+ \mu \frac{k}{r} (d\delta\mathbf{h} \wedge \mathbf{h} + \delta\mathbf{h}d\mathbf{h} - \mathcal{L}(\mathbf{h})\cdot d\mathbf{h}) = 0. \qquad (39\text{-}4)$$

It is simpler to multiply (39-3) by r. We have then

$$i(r\mathbf{u})\Pi + \frac{Tr}{c^2} dS + \frac{\mu r^2}{2} \cdot d\frac{|\mathbf{h}|^2}{r^2}$$

$$+ \mu(\delta\mathbf{h}\cdot\mathbf{h} - \mathcal{L}(\mathbf{h})\mathbf{h} - \tfrac{1}{2} d|\mathbf{h}|^2) = 0.$$

The Lie derivative of Π with respect to the vector $r\mathbf{u}$ is then given by

$$\mathcal{L}(r\mathbf{u})\Pi + \frac{1}{c^2} d(Tr) \wedge dS + \mu r dr \wedge d\left(\frac{|\mathbf{h}|^2}{r^2}\right)$$

$$+ \mu(d\delta\mathbf{h} \wedge \mathbf{h} + \delta\mathbf{h}d\mathbf{h} - \mathcal{L}(\mathbf{h})d\mathbf{h}) = 0, \qquad (39\text{-}5)$$

which is a relatively simple system of equations of the Helmholtz type.

(**c**) Let us consider, for example, *an incoherent fluid*, with $p = 0$ and $\epsilon = 0$. We have in this case

$$f = 1, \qquad S = \text{const.},$$

and according to (34-12),

$$\delta\mathbf{h} = 0.$$

Under these assumptions, (39-5) can be written in the simple way,

$$\mathcal{L}(r\mathbf{u})\Pi + \mu r dr \wedge d\left(\frac{|\mathbf{h}|^2}{r^2}\right) - \mu\mathcal{L}(\mathbf{h})d\mathbf{h} = 0. \qquad (39\text{-}6)$$

40. Representation of the Wave Cones in R^3

(**a**) In each point x of V_4, we have, according to §35, three cones with the equations:

$$\Gamma : g^{\lambda\mu}\,\xi_\lambda\,\xi_\mu = 0;$$

$$\Gamma_H : P^{\lambda\mu\nu\rho}\,\xi_\lambda\,\xi_\mu\,\xi_\nu\,\xi_\rho = 0;$$

$$\Gamma_A : Q^{\lambda\mu}\,\xi_\lambda\,\xi_\mu = 0.$$

Let us consider in x an orthonormalized rest frame $\{\mathbf{v}_{(\rho)}\}$ with

$$\mathbf{v}_{(0)} = \mathbf{u}, \qquad \mathbf{v}_{(3)} = \frac{\mathbf{h}}{|\mathbf{h}|}.$$

We set

$$\xi_0 = t, \qquad \xi_1 = x, \qquad \xi_2 = y, \qquad \xi_3 = z.$$

With these notations, we have, for the three cones, the equations

$$\begin{cases} \Gamma : t^2 - x^2 - y^2 - z^2 = 0, \\ \Gamma_H : rf(\gamma - 1)t^4 + (rf + \mu\,|\mathbf{h}|^2\gamma)\,t^2\,(t^2 - x^2 - y^2 - z^2) \\ \qquad\qquad - \mu\,|\mathbf{h}|^2 z^2\,(t^2 - x^2 - y^2 - z^2) = 0, \\ \Gamma_A : (rf + \mu\,|\mathbf{h}|^2)t^2 - \mu\,|\mathbf{h}|^2 z^2 = 0, \end{cases}$$

where

$$\gamma = \frac{fr'_f}{r} > 1. \tag{40-1}$$

We set, in the following part,

$$\beta = \frac{rf}{\mu\,|\mathbf{h}|^2} > 0 \tag{40-2}$$

and we then obtain the equations

$$\begin{cases} \Gamma : t^2 - x^2 - y^2 - z^2 = 0, \\ \Gamma_H : \beta(\gamma - 1)t^4 + (\beta + \gamma)t^2(t^2 - x^2 - y^2 - z^2) \\ \qquad - z^2(t^2 - x^2 - y^2 - z^2) = 0. \\ \Gamma_A : (\beta + 1)t^2 - z^2 = 0. \end{cases}$$

We call "*indicatrices in* R^3" the sections of these cones with the hyperplane $t = 1$. We obtain thus the three following indicatrices

$$\begin{cases} S : 1 - x^2 - y^2 - z^2 = 0, \\ S_H : (\beta + 1)\gamma - (\beta + \gamma)(x^2 + y^2 + z^2) \\ \qquad - z^2(1 - x^2 - y^2 - z^2) = 0, \\ S_A : z^2 = \beta + 1. \end{cases}$$

(b) Let us discuss the form of these indicatrices; $0z$ is an axis of rotation and it is sufficient to cut the indicatrices by the plane $x = 0$. We obtain for the sphere S, the circle

$$y^2 + z^2 = 1,$$

for the two planes S_A, the two straight lines

$$z^2 = \beta + 1,$$

and for S_H, the quartic curve

$$C_H : (\beta + 1)\gamma - (\beta + \gamma)(y^2 + z^2) - z^2(1 - y^2 - z^2) = 0,$$

which has $0y$ and $0z$ as axis of symmetry. The equation of C_H can be written

$$y^2 = -\frac{[z^2 - \gamma][z^2 - (\beta + 1)]}{z^2 - (\beta + \gamma)}. \tag{40-3}$$

For $z^2 = 0$, we have

$$y^2 = \frac{(\beta + 1)\gamma}{\beta + \gamma}.$$

For $z^2 = \gamma$ and $z^2 = (\beta + 1)$, we have $y^2 = 0$, and the curve C_H admits the asymptotes $z^2 = \beta + \gamma$.

It is easy to see that for $\gamma \neq \beta + 1$, for example, for $\gamma < \beta + 1$, we have for C_H the form of Fig. (40-1). If $\gamma = \beta + 1$, we have singular points on 0z and, thus, the form of Fig. 40-2. Thus *in the general case* $(\gamma \neq \beta + 1)$, Γ_H is decomposed in two parts, Γ_{H_1} and Γ_{H_2}; the exterior part Γ_{H_1} corresponds to the slow waves and the interior part Γ_{H_2} to the fast waves.

In the special case $\gamma = \beta + 1$, that is,

$$\frac{v_0^2}{c^2} = \frac{\mu\,|\mathbf{h}|^2}{rf + \mu\,|\mathbf{h}|^2},$$

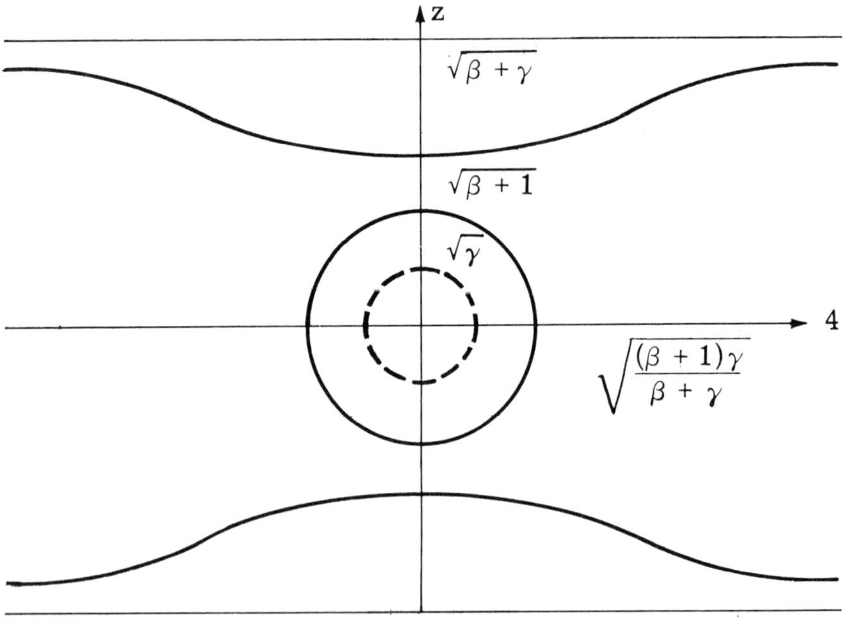

Figure 40-1

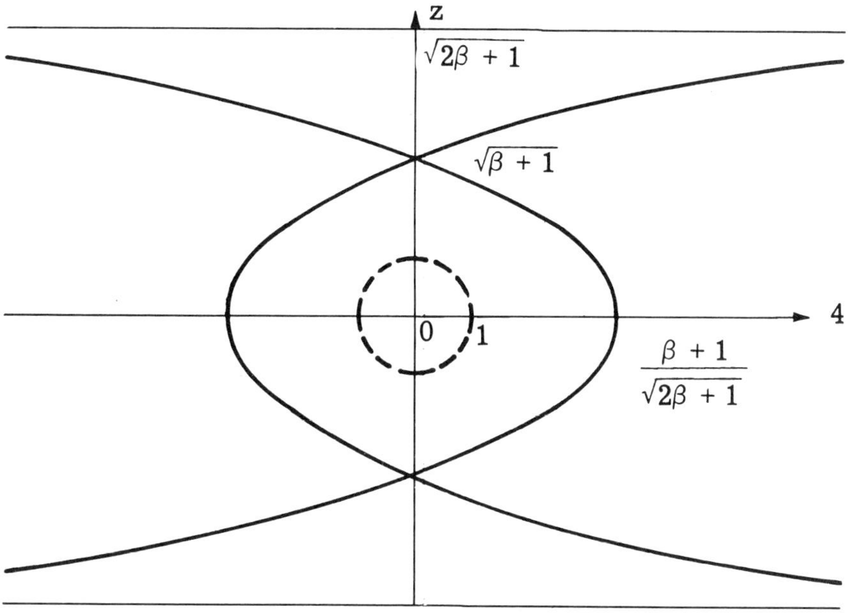

Figure 40-2

the conic hypersurface Γ_H has two singular generatrices $x = 0,\ y = 0,\ z^2 = (\beta + 1)t^2$ contained in the 2-plane Π defined by $(\mathbf{u}, \mathbf{h})$. In all cases, the conic hypersurface Γ_A is the set of the two hyperplanes $z = \pm\sqrt{\beta + 1}\,t$, the intersection of which is the 2-plane Π' defined by $z = 0$, $t = 0$, that is, the 2-plane orthogonal to the 2-plane Π defined by $(\mathbf{u}, \mathbf{h})$.

We note that *if* $\gamma = 1$, *that is, if the fluid is incompressible*, the part Γ_{H_1} corresponding to the slow waves coincides with Γ_A, and the part Γ_{H_2} coincides with Γ.

(**c**) We study now the intersection $\Gamma_H \cap \Gamma_A$. If we set $z^2 = (\beta + 1)t^2$ in the equation of Γ_H,

$$\gamma(\beta + 1)t^4 - (\beta + 1 + \gamma)z^2t^2 + z^4$$

$$- (x^2 + y^2)\left[(\beta + \gamma)t^2 - z^2\right] = 0,$$

we obtain

$$t^2\{[\gamma(\beta + 1) - (\beta + 1 + \gamma)(\beta + 1) + (\beta + 1)^2]t^2$$
$$- (x^2 + y^2)(\beta + \gamma - \beta - 1)\} = 0,$$

that is,

$$(\gamma - 1)t^2(x^2 + y^2) = 0.$$

We obtain for the intersection, the 2-plane Π' and the generatrices of Γ_H contained in the 2-plane Π and defined by $z^2 = (\beta + 1)t^2$. In the general case ($\gamma \neq \beta + 1$), the hyperplanes Γ_A are tangent to Γ_H along these generatrices; but in the special case $\gamma = \beta + 1$, we have seen these generatrices are singular.

Let us consider also the hyperplane,

$$u^\rho \xi_\rho = 0,$$

which corresponds to the characteristics generated by the stream lines. In our frame, it is the hyperplane $t = 0$ and its intersection either with Γ_H or with each hyperplane of Γ_A which is *the 2-plane* Π'.

(d) From the previous considerations, it follows that *in the general case* ($\gamma \neq \beta + 1$), *the conic hypersurface* Γ_H *is such that the corresponding operator* $P^{\lambda\mu\nu\rho}\partial_{\lambda\mu\nu\rho}$ *is strictly hyperbolic*. But the decomposition of Γ_A in two hyperplanes, the intersection of which is the 2-plane Π', shows that *the operator* $Q^{\lambda\mu}\partial_{\lambda\mu}$ *is not strictly hyperbolic, but is the product of two strictly hyperbolic operators corresponding to the two hyperplanes*. If we consider the interiors of the half-cones defined by the operators $g^{\lambda\mu}\partial_{\lambda\mu}$, $P^{\lambda\mu\nu\rho}\partial_{\lambda\mu\nu\rho}$, $Q^{\lambda\mu}\partial_{\lambda\mu}$, and $u^\rho\partial_\rho$, we see that the intersection of these interiors is the interior of the dual of the elementary half-cone.

If $\gamma = \beta + 1$, *the operator* $P^{\lambda\mu\nu\rho}\partial_{\lambda\mu\nu\rho}$ *is not strictly hyperbolic.*

41. Auxiliary Equations, Consequences of the Main System [9]

(a) Our purpose, now, is to give a mathematical study of the main system (35-1), (35-2), (35-3), (35-4), (35-5) of the relativistic magnetohydrodynamics. In the following part, this system is called system (I).

We have seen that, for convenient initial data, the system (I) is equivalent to the system (35-4), (35-12), (35-13), (35-14), (35-15) which is now called system (II). We will prove that there exists a system, a consequence of the system (II), which is a *Leray system*, but, of course, which is *not strictly hyperbolic*. The construction of this Leray system is relatively long, but the method is very similar to the method given in §16.

(b) First, we will construct some auxiliary equations which are direct consequences of the system (II). To simplify the notations in the following part, we set

$$a = \nabla_\alpha u^\alpha, \qquad b = \nabla_\alpha h^\alpha, \tag{41-1}$$

and we introduce systematically the variables $g_{\alpha\beta}$, f, S, u^α, h^α. We write the interesting equations with these notations.

From the consequences (32-9) and (32-11) of the Maxwell equations, we have

$$b = u^\alpha u^\beta \nabla_\alpha h_\beta \tag{41-2}$$

and

$$\tfrac{1}{2} u^\alpha \nabla_\alpha |\mathbf{h}|^2 + a|\mathbf{h}|^2 - h^\alpha \cdot u^\beta \nabla_\alpha h_\beta = 0. \tag{41-3}$$

The equation (34-13) can be written

$$b = -\frac{h^\alpha}{f}\left(\partial_\alpha f - \frac{T}{c^2}\partial_\alpha S\right)$$

$$= A(1 \text{ in } f,\ 1 \text{ in } S,\ 0 \text{ in } h^\alpha), \tag{41-4}$$

and the equation of continuity (35-13) can be written

$$a = -\frac{r'_f}{r} u^\alpha \partial_\alpha f$$

$$= B(1 \text{ in } f,\ 0 \text{ in } S,\ 0 \text{ in } u^\alpha) \tag{41-5}$$

according to (35-4).

Now the system of the stream lines can be written

$$u^\alpha \nabla_\alpha u^\beta = C^\beta (1 \text{ in } g_{\alpha\beta},\ 1 \text{ in } f,\ 1 \text{ in } S,\ 0 \text{ in } u^\alpha,\ 1 \text{ in } h^\alpha), \tag{41-6}$$

and the system of the Maxwell equations, according to (41-5), can be written

$$h^\alpha \nabla_\alpha u^\beta = u^\alpha \nabla_\alpha h^\beta + ah^\beta - bu^\beta$$

$$= D^\beta (1 \text{ in } g_{\alpha\beta},\ 1 \text{ in } f,\ 1 \text{ in } S,\ 0 \text{ in } u^\alpha,\ 1 \text{ in } h^\alpha). \tag{41-7}$$

(c) From (41-3), we deduce by derivation along the stream lines,

$$\tfrac{1}{2} u^\alpha u^\beta \nabla_\alpha \nabla_\beta |\mathbf{h}|^2 + \tfrac{1}{2} u^\beta \nabla_\beta u^\alpha \nabla_\alpha |\mathbf{h}|^2 + au^\beta \nabla_\beta |\mathbf{h}|^2$$
$$+ |\mathbf{h}|^2 u^\beta \nabla_\beta a - h^\lambda u^\mu u^\beta \nabla_\beta \nabla_\lambda h_\mu$$
$$- u^\beta \nabla_\beta h^\lambda u^\mu \nabla_\lambda h_\mu - h^\lambda u^\beta \nabla_\beta u^\mu \nabla_\lambda h_\mu = 0.$$

It follows from (41-6) and (41-3) that we obtain an equation of the form

$$\tfrac{1}{2} u^\alpha u^\beta \nabla_\alpha \nabla_\beta |\mathbf{h}|^2 + |\mathbf{h}|^2 u^\beta \nabla_\beta a - h^\lambda u^\mu u^\beta \nabla_\beta \nabla_\lambda h_\mu$$
$$= E(1 \text{ in } g_{\alpha\beta},\ 1 \text{ in } f,\ 1 \text{ in } S,\ 0 \text{ in } u^\alpha,\ 1 \text{ in } h^\alpha).$$

According to the Ricci identity, we have

$$h^\lambda u^\mu u^\beta \nabla_\beta \nabla_\lambda h_\mu = h^\lambda u^\mu u^\beta \nabla_\lambda \nabla_\beta h_\mu + F(2 \text{ in } g_{\alpha\beta},\ 0 \text{ in } u^\alpha,\ 0 \text{ in } h^\alpha),$$

or, according to the Maxwell equations (41-7),

$$h^\lambda u^\mu u^\beta \nabla_\beta \nabla_\lambda h_\mu = h^\lambda \nabla_\lambda (u^\beta u^\mu \nabla_\beta h_\mu) + G(2 \text{ in } g_{\alpha\beta},\ 1 \text{ in } f,\ 1 \text{ in } S,\ 0 \text{ in } u^\alpha,\ 1 \text{ in } h^\alpha).$$

We thus obtain

$$h^\lambda u^\mu u^\beta \nabla_\beta \nabla_\lambda h_\mu = h^\lambda \nabla_\lambda b + G(2 \text{ in } g_{\alpha\beta},\ 1 \text{ in } f,\ 1 \text{ in } S,\ 0 \text{ in } u^\alpha,\ 1 \text{ in } h^\alpha),$$

and so, using this last equation, (41-8) can be written

$$\tfrac{1}{2} u^\alpha u^\beta \nabla_\alpha \nabla_\beta |\mathbf{h}|^2 + |\mathbf{h}|^2 u^\beta \nabla_\beta a - h^\beta \nabla_\beta b = H(2 \text{ in } g_{\alpha\beta},\ 1 \text{ in } f,\ 1 \text{ in } S,\ 0 \text{ in } u^\alpha,\ 1 \text{ in } h^\alpha). \qquad (41\text{-}9)$$

It follows from (41-4) that (41-9) can be written

$$\tfrac{1}{2} u^\alpha u^\beta \nabla_\alpha \nabla_\beta |\mathbf{h}|^2 + |\mathbf{h}|^2 u^\beta \nabla_\beta a + h^\beta \nabla_\beta \left[\frac{h^\alpha \nabla_\alpha f}{f} - \frac{T}{c^2 f} h^\alpha \nabla_\alpha S\right] = H(2 \text{ in } g_{\alpha\beta},\ 1 \text{ in } f,\ 1 \text{ in } S,\ 0 \text{ in } u^\alpha,\ 1 \text{ in } h^\alpha),$$

that is,

$$\tfrac{1}{2}\, u^{\alpha} u^{\beta} \nabla_{\alpha} \nabla_{\beta} |\mathbf{h}|^2 + \frac{h^{\alpha} h^{\beta}}{f} \nabla_{\alpha} \nabla_{\beta} f$$

$$+ |\mathbf{h}|^2 u^{\beta} \nabla_{\beta} a - \frac{T}{c^2 f} h^{\alpha} h^{\beta} \nabla_{\alpha} \nabla_{\beta} S$$

$$= I(2 \text{ in } g_{\alpha\beta},\ 1 \text{ in } f,\ 1 \text{ in } S,\ 0 \text{ in } u^{\alpha},\ 1 \text{ in } h^{\alpha}). \tag{41-10}$$

From (41-5), we deduce by derivation along the stream lines,

$$u^{\beta} \nabla_{\beta} a = -\frac{r'_f}{r} u^{\alpha} u^{\beta} \nabla_{\alpha} \nabla_{\beta} f - \frac{r'_f}{r} u^{\beta} \nabla_{\beta} u^{\alpha} \nabla_{\alpha} f$$

$$- u^{\beta} \nabla_{\beta} \left(\frac{r'_f}{r}\right) u^{\alpha} \partial_{\alpha} f,$$

that is,

$$u^{\beta} \nabla_{\beta} a = -\frac{r'_f}{r} u^{\alpha} u^{\beta} \nabla_{\alpha} \nabla_{\beta} f$$

$$+ J(1 \text{ in } g_{\alpha\beta},\ 1 \text{ in } f,\ 1 \text{ in } S,\ 0 \text{ in } u^{\alpha},\ 1 \text{ in } h^{\alpha}). \tag{41-11}$$

If we use (41-11) in (41-10), we obtain the first sought for equation,

$$\tfrac{1}{2}\, r f u^{\alpha} u^{\beta} \nabla_{\alpha} \nabla_{\beta} |\mathbf{h}|^2 + (r h^{\alpha} h^{\beta} - |\mathbf{h}|^2 f r'_f u^{\alpha} u^{\beta}) \nabla_{\alpha} \nabla_{\beta} f$$

$$- \frac{rT}{c^2} h^{\alpha} h^{\beta} \nabla_{\alpha} \nabla_{\beta} S$$

$$= K(2 \text{ in } g_{\alpha\beta},\ 1 \text{ in } f,\ 1 \text{ in } S,\ 0 \text{ in } u^{\alpha},\ 1 \text{ in } h^{\alpha}). \tag{41-12}$$

(d) We consider now the equations of the stream lines,

$$(rf + \mu |\mathbf{h}|^2) u^\alpha \nabla_\alpha u^\beta - (g^{\alpha\beta} - u^\alpha u^\beta)$$
$$\times \left(r \partial_\alpha f + \tfrac{1}{2} \mu \partial_\alpha |\mathbf{h}|^2 - \frac{rT}{c^2} \partial_\alpha S \right)$$
$$+ \tfrac{1}{2} \mu u^\alpha \nabla_\alpha |\mathbf{h}|^2 u^\beta + \mu a |\mathbf{h}|^2 u^\beta$$
$$- \mu b h^\beta - \mu h^\alpha \nabla_\alpha h^\beta = 0,$$

and we introduce the contracted derivative of these equations. According to the Ricci identity, we obtain an equation of the form

$$(rf + \mu |\mathbf{h}|^2) u^\alpha \nabla_\alpha a - (g^{\alpha\beta} - u^\alpha u^\beta)$$
$$\times \left(r \nabla_\alpha \nabla_\beta f - \frac{rT}{c^2} \nabla_\alpha \nabla_\beta S \right)$$
$$- \tfrac{1}{2} (g^{\alpha\beta} - u^\alpha u^\beta) \mu \nabla_\alpha \nabla_\beta |\mathbf{h}|^2$$
$$+ \tfrac{1}{2} \mu u^\alpha u^\beta \nabla_\alpha \nabla_\beta |\mathbf{h}|^2 + \mu |\mathbf{h}|^2 u^\beta \nabla_\beta a - 2\mu h^\beta \nabla_\beta b$$
$$= L(2 \text{ in } g_{\alpha\beta}, 1 \text{ in } f, 1 \text{ in } S, 1 \text{ in } u^\alpha, 1 \text{ in } h^\alpha)$$

This equation can be written

$$rf u^\alpha \nabla_\alpha a - (g^{\alpha\beta} - u^\alpha u^\beta) \left(r \nabla_\alpha \nabla_\beta f - \frac{rT}{c^2} \nabla_\alpha \nabla_\beta S \right)$$
$$- \tfrac{1}{2} \mu g^{\alpha\beta} \nabla_\alpha \nabla_\beta |\mathbf{h}|^2$$
$$+ \mu [u^\alpha u^\beta \nabla_\alpha \nabla_\beta |\mathbf{h}|^2 + 2 |\mathbf{h}|^2 u^\beta \nabla_\beta a - 2 h^\beta \nabla_\beta b]$$
$$= L(2 \text{ in } g_{\alpha\beta}, 1 \text{ in } f, 1 \text{ in } S, 1 \text{ in } u^\alpha, 1 \text{ in } h^\alpha),$$

that is, according to (41-9),

$$rfu^\alpha \nabla_\alpha a - (g^{\alpha\beta} - u^\alpha u^\beta)\left(r\nabla_\alpha \nabla_\beta f - \frac{rT}{c^2} \nabla_\alpha \nabla_\beta S\right)$$

$$- \tfrac{1}{2}\, \mu g^{\alpha\beta} \nabla_\alpha \nabla_\beta |\mathbf{h}|^2$$

$$= M(2 \text{ in } g_{\alpha\beta},\ 1 \text{ in } f,\ 1 \text{ in } S,\ 1 \text{ in } u^\alpha,\ 1 \text{ in } h^\alpha).$$

If we substitute into this equation, the expression (41-5) for a, we obtain

$$-fr'_f u^\alpha u^\beta \nabla_\alpha \nabla_\beta f - (g^{\alpha\beta} - u^\alpha u^\beta)$$

$$\times \left(r\nabla_\alpha \nabla_\beta f - \frac{rT}{c^2} \nabla_\alpha \nabla_\beta S\right) - \tfrac{1}{2}\, \mu g^{\alpha\beta} \nabla_\alpha \nabla_\beta |\mathbf{h}|^2$$

$$= -N(2 \text{ in } g_{\alpha\beta},\ 1 \text{ in } f,\ 1 \text{ in } S,\ 1 \text{ in } u^\alpha,\ 1 \text{ in } h^\alpha).$$

This yields the second sought - for equation

$$\tfrac{1}{2}\, \mu g^{\alpha\beta} \nabla_\alpha \nabla_\beta |\mathbf{h}|^2 + [r(g^{\alpha\beta} - u^\alpha u^\beta)$$

$$+ fr'_f u^\alpha u^\beta] \nabla_\alpha \nabla_\beta f - \frac{rT}{c^2} (g^{\alpha\beta} - u^\alpha u^\beta) \nabla_\alpha \nabla_\beta S$$

$$= N(2 \text{ in } g_{\alpha\beta},\ 1 \text{ in } f,\ 1 \text{ in } S,\ 1 \text{ in } u^\alpha,\ 1 \text{ in } h^\alpha). \tag{41-13}$$

42. The Equations Corresponding to f and $|\mathbf{h}|^2$

We can deduce from the relations (41-12) and (41-13) two important equations concerning, respectively, the propagation of the scalars f and $|\mathbf{h}|^2$.

(a) First, we multiply (41-13) by the operator

$$rfu^\lambda u^\mu \nabla_\lambda \nabla_\mu,$$

which appears in (41-12) acting on $|\mathbf{h}|^2$. According to (41-12), we obtain,

$$\{[r(g^{\alpha\beta} - u^\alpha u^\beta) + fr'_f u^\alpha u^\beta]rfu^\lambda u^\mu$$

$$+ \mu g^{\alpha\beta}(|\mathbf{h}|^2 fr'_f u^\lambda u^\mu - \mu h^\lambda h^\mu)\}$$

$$\times \partial_{\alpha\beta\lambda\mu} f - \frac{rT}{c^2}\{(g^{\alpha\beta} - u^\alpha u^\beta) rfu^\lambda u^\mu$$

$$- ug^{\alpha\beta} h^\lambda h^\mu\} \partial_{\alpha\beta\lambda\mu} S$$

$$= P(4 \text{ in } g_{\alpha\beta}, 3 \text{ in f}, 3 \text{ in S}, 3 \text{ in } u^\alpha, 3 \text{ in } h^\alpha).$$

Using the identity

$$u^\rho \partial_{\lambda\mu\nu\rho} S = \partial_{\lambda\mu\nu}(u^\rho \partial_\rho S) + Z(3 \text{ in S}, 3 \text{ in } u^\alpha),$$

it is possible to write the above equation in the form,

$$\left\{[fr'_f - r]u^\lambda u^\mu u^\nu u^\rho + \left(r + \mu|\mathbf{h}|^2 \frac{r'_f}{r}\right) g^{(\lambda\mu} u^\nu u^{\rho)}\right.$$

$$\left. - \frac{\mu}{f} g^{(\lambda\mu} h^\nu h^{\rho)}\right\} \left(\partial_{\lambda\mu\nu\rho} f - \frac{T}{c^2} \partial_{\lambda\mu\nu\rho} S\right)$$

$$= Q(4 \text{ in } g_{\alpha\beta}, 3 \text{ in f}, 3 \text{ in S}, 3 \text{ in } u^\alpha, 3 \text{ in } h^\alpha).$$

We have thus obtained, according to (35-28), *the following equation concerning* f:

$$P^{\lambda\mu\nu\rho} \partial_{\lambda\mu\nu\rho} f - \frac{T}{c^2} P^{\lambda\mu\nu\rho} \partial_{\lambda\mu\nu\rho} S$$

$$= Q(4 \text{ in } g_{\alpha\beta}, 3 \text{ in f}, 3 \text{ in S}, 3 \text{ in } u^\alpha, 3 \text{ in } h^\alpha). \tag{42-1}$$

(b) Now, we come back to the relations (41-12) and (41-13). We multiply (41-13) by the operator $(|\mathbf{h}|^2 fr'_f u^\lambda u^\mu - rh^\lambda h^\mu) \nabla_\lambda \nabla_\mu$ which appears in (41-12) acting on the scalar f. According to (41-12), we obtain

$$\tfrac{1}{2}\{\mu g^{\alpha\beta}(|\mathbf{h}|^2 fr'_f u^\lambda u^\mu - rh^\lambda h^\mu) + [r(g^{\alpha\beta} - u^\alpha u^\beta)$$
$$+ fr'_f u^\alpha u^\beta] rfu^\lambda u^\mu\}\, \partial_{\alpha\beta\lambda\mu} |\mathbf{h}|^2$$
$$- \frac{rT}{c^2}\{(g^{\alpha\beta} - u^\alpha u^\beta)(|\mathbf{h}|^2 fr'_f u^\lambda u^\mu - rh^\lambda h^\mu)$$
$$+ h^\lambda h^\mu [r(g^{\alpha\beta} - u^\alpha u^\beta) + fr'_f u^\alpha u^\beta]\}\, \partial_{\alpha\beta\lambda\mu} S$$
$$= R(4 \text{ in } g_{\alpha\beta},\ 3 \text{ in } f,\ 3 \text{ in } S,\ 3 \text{ in } u^\alpha,\ 3 \text{ in } h^\alpha),$$

that is,

$$\tfrac{1}{2}\, rfP^{\lambda\mu\nu\rho}\, \partial_{\lambda\mu\nu\rho} |\mathbf{h}|^2 - \frac{rT}{c^2}[(g^{\lambda\mu} - u^\lambda u^\mu)|\mathbf{h}|^2 fr'_f u^\nu u^\rho$$
$$+ fr'_f h^\lambda h^\mu u^\nu u^\rho]\, \partial_{\lambda\mu\nu\rho} S$$
$$= R(4 \text{ in } g_{\alpha\beta},\ 3 \text{ in } f,\ 3 \text{ in } S,\ 3 \text{ in } u^\alpha,\ 3 \text{ in } h^\alpha).$$

According to $u^\rho \partial_\rho S = 0$, it follows that we have *the following equation concerning* $|\mathbf{h}|^2$:

$$P^{\lambda\mu\nu\rho}\, \partial_{\lambda\mu\nu\rho} |\mathbf{h}|^2$$
$$= R_1(4 \text{ in } g_{\alpha\beta},\ 3 \text{ in } f,\ 3 \text{ in } S,\ 3 \text{ in } u^\alpha,$$
$$3 \text{ in } h^\alpha). \qquad (42\text{-}2)$$

43. The Equations Corresponding to the μ^α

We consider the Maxwell equations,

$$u^\alpha \nabla_\alpha h^\tau - h^\alpha \nabla_\alpha u^\tau + ah^\tau - bu^\tau = 0, \qquad (43\text{-}1)$$

and the equations of the stream lines,

$$\text{rku}^{\alpha} \nabla_{\alpha} u^{\tau} - (g^{\alpha\tau} - u^{\alpha} u^{\tau}) \left(r\, \partial_{\alpha} f - \frac{rT}{c^2}\, \partial_{\alpha} S \right)$$

$$- \tfrac{1}{2}\, \mu g^{\alpha\tau} \nabla_{\alpha} |\mathbf{h}|^2 + \mu u^{\alpha} u^{\tau} \nabla_{\alpha} |\mathbf{h}|^2$$

$$+ \mu a |\mathbf{h}|^2 u^{\tau} - \mu b h^{\tau} - \mu h^{\alpha} \nabla_{\alpha} h^{\tau} = 0, \tag{43-2}$$

where $rk = rf + \mu |\mathbf{h}|^2$. If we multiply (43-1) by $h^{\beta} \nabla_{\beta}$, we obtain

$$u^{\alpha} h^{\beta} \nabla_{\beta} \nabla_{\alpha} h^{\tau} - h^{\alpha} h^{\beta} \nabla_{\alpha} \nabla_{\beta} u^{\tau} + h^{\tau} h^{\beta} \nabla_{\beta} a - u^{\tau} h^{\beta} \nabla_{\beta} b$$

$$= A^{\tau} (1 \text{ in } g_{\alpha\beta},\ 1 \text{ in } u^{\alpha},\ 1 \text{ in } h^{\alpha}). \tag{43-3}$$

Similarly, if we multiply (43-2) by $u^{\beta} \nabla_{\beta}$, we have according to $u^{\beta} \partial_{\beta} S = 0$,

$$\text{rku}^{\alpha} u^{\beta} \nabla_{\alpha} \nabla_{\beta} u^{\tau} - (g^{\alpha\tau} - u^{\alpha} u^{\tau})(r u^{\beta} \nabla_{\alpha} \nabla_{\beta} f)$$

$$- \tfrac{1}{2}\, \mu g^{\alpha\tau} u^{\beta} \nabla_{\alpha} \nabla_{\beta} |\mathbf{h}|^2 + \mu u^{\tau} u^{\alpha} u^{\beta} \nabla_{\alpha} \nabla_{\beta} |\mathbf{h}|^2$$

$$+ \mu |\mathbf{h}|^2 u^{\tau} u^{\beta} \nabla_{\beta} a - \mu h^{\tau} u^{\beta} \nabla_{\beta} b$$

$$- \mu h^{\alpha} u^{\beta} \nabla_{\beta} \nabla_{\alpha} h^{\tau}$$

$$= B^{\tau} (1 \text{ in } g_{\alpha\beta},\ 1 \text{ in } f,\ 1 \text{ in } S,\ 1 \text{ in } u^{\alpha},\ 1 \text{ in } h^{\alpha}). \tag{43-4}$$

By multiplication of (43-3) by μ and by addition to (43-4), we obtain, according to the Ricci identity for h^{τ},

$$(\text{rku}^{\alpha} u^{\beta} - \mu h^{\alpha} h^{\beta}) \nabla_{\alpha} \nabla_{\beta} u^{\tau} - \tfrac{1}{2}\, \mu g^{\alpha\tau} u^{\beta} \nabla_{\alpha} \nabla_{\beta} |\mathbf{h}|^2$$

$$+ \mu u^{\tau} u^{\alpha} u^{\beta} \nabla_{\alpha} \nabla_{\beta} |\mathbf{h}|^2 + \mu [h^{\tau} h^{\beta} \nabla_{\beta} a$$

$$+ |\mathbf{h}|^2 u^{\tau} u^{\beta} \nabla_{\beta} a - u^{\tau} h^{\beta} \nabla_{\beta} b - h^{\tau} u^{\beta} \nabla_{\beta} b]$$

$$- (g^{\alpha\tau} - u^{\alpha} u^{\tau})\, r u^{\beta} \nabla_{\alpha} \nabla_{\beta} f$$

$$= C^{\tau} (2 \text{ in } g_{\alpha\beta},\ 1 \text{ in } f,\ 1 \text{ in } S,\ 1 \text{ in } u^{\alpha},\ 1 \text{ in } h^{\alpha}).$$

But, it follows from (41-5) that $\nabla_\beta a$ depends only on the second derivatives of f and on the first derivatives of S and the u^α. Similarly, according to (41-4), $\nabla_\beta b$ depends only on the second derivatives of f and S and on the first derivatives of the u^α. It follows that

$$(rku^\alpha u^\beta - \mu h^\alpha h^\beta)\nabla_\alpha\nabla_\beta u^\tau - \tfrac{1}{2}\mu g^{\alpha\tau}u^\beta\nabla_\alpha\nabla_\beta|\mathbf{h}|^2$$

$$+ \mu u^\tau u^\alpha u^\beta \nabla_\alpha\nabla_\beta|\mathbf{h}|^2$$

$$= D^\tau(2 \text{ in } g_{\alpha\beta},\ 2 \text{ in f},\ 2 \text{ in S},\ 1 \text{ in } u^\alpha,\ 1 \text{ in } h^\alpha).$$

But, it follows from (41-12) that $u^\alpha u^\beta \nabla_\alpha\nabla_\beta|\mathbf{h}|^2$ depends only on the same derivatives which appear in the right-hand side of the above equation. We obtain thus the interesting equations in which appears the wave operator $Q^{\lambda\mu}\partial_{\lambda\mu}$:

$$Q^{\lambda\mu}\nabla_\lambda\nabla_\mu u^\tau - \tfrac{1}{2}\mu g^{\alpha\tau}u^\beta\nabla_\alpha\nabla_\beta|\mathbf{h}|^2$$

$$= E^\tau(2 \text{ in } g_{\alpha\beta},\ 2 \text{ in f},\ 2 \text{ in S},\ 1 \text{ in } u^\alpha,\ 1 \text{ in } h^\alpha).$$

44. A Lemma

The following lemma is useful for the construction of our new system.

Lemma. If we consider as unknown functions the functions $g_{\alpha\beta}$, f, S, $|\mathbf{h}|^2$, u^α, *and* h^α, *then the scalar* $u^\alpha u^\beta\nabla_\alpha\nabla_\beta|\mathbf{h}|^2$ *satisfies a relation of the form:*

$$P^{\lambda\mu\nu\rho}\partial_{\lambda\mu\nu\rho}(u^\alpha u^\beta\nabla_\alpha\nabla_\beta|\mathbf{h}|^2)$$

$$= X(6 \text{ in } g_{\alpha\beta},\ 5 \text{ in f},\ 5 \text{ in } |\mathbf{h}|^2,\ 5 \text{ in S},\ 5 \text{ in } u^\alpha,\ 4 \text{ in } h^\alpha). \tag{44-1}$$

(a) To prove the existence of this relation, we consider the equation (41-3). Let

$$\tfrac{1}{2}u^\alpha\nabla_\alpha|\mathbf{h}|^2 + a|\mathbf{h}|^2 - h^\lambda u^\mu\nabla_\lambda h_\mu = 0.$$

If we multiply by $u^\beta \nabla_\beta$, we obtain explicitly

$$\tfrac{1}{2} u^\alpha u^\beta \nabla_\alpha \nabla_\beta |\mathbf{h}|^2 + \tfrac{1}{2} u^\beta \nabla_\beta u^\alpha \nabla_\alpha |\mathbf{h}|^2 + u^\beta \nabla_\beta (a |\mathbf{h}|^2) - u^\beta \nabla_\beta h^\lambda u^\mu \nabla_\lambda h_\mu - h^\lambda u^\beta \nabla_\beta u^\mu \nabla_\lambda h_\mu - h^\lambda u^\mu u^\beta \nabla_\beta \nabla_\lambda h_\mu = 0,$$

that is,

$$\tfrac{1}{2} u^\alpha u^\beta \nabla_\alpha \nabla_\beta |\mathbf{h}|^2 + \tfrac{1}{2} u^\beta \nabla_\beta u^\alpha \nabla_\alpha |\mathbf{h}|^2 + |\mathbf{h}|^2 u^\beta \nabla_\beta a + a u^\beta \nabla_\beta |\mathbf{h}|^2 + u^\beta \nabla_\beta h^\lambda h^\mu \nabla_\lambda u_\mu - h^\lambda \nabla_\lambda h_\mu u^\beta \nabla_\beta u^\mu - h^\lambda u^\mu u^\beta \nabla_\beta \nabla_\lambda h_\mu = 0. \qquad (44\text{-}1)$$

But, according to the Maxwell equations and the expression (41-4) of b, we have

$$u^\beta \nabla_\beta h^\lambda = A^\lambda (1 \text{ in } g_{\alpha\beta},\ 1 \text{ in f},\ 1 \text{ in S},\ 1 \text{ in } u^\alpha,\ 0 \text{ in } h^\alpha). \qquad (44\text{-}2)$$

The equations of the stream lines (43-2) give, similarly,

$$h^\lambda \nabla_\lambda h_\mu = -\tfrac{1}{2} \nabla_\mu |\mathbf{h}|^2 + u_\mu u^\alpha \nabla_\alpha |\mathbf{h}|^2 + B_\mu (1 \text{ in } g_{\alpha\beta},\ 1 \text{ in f},\ 1 \text{ in S},\ 1 \text{ in } u^\alpha,\ 0 \text{ in } h^\alpha). \qquad (44\text{-}3)$$

Moreover, according to the Ricci identity, we have

$$u^\mu u^\beta \nabla_\beta \nabla_\lambda h_\mu = \nabla_\lambda (u^\mu u^\beta \nabla_\beta h_\mu) + C_\lambda (2 \text{ in } g_{\alpha\beta},\ 1 \text{ in } u^\alpha,\ 0 \text{ in } h^\alpha),$$

that is, if we use (41-2),

$$u^\mu u^\beta \nabla_\beta \nabla_\lambda h_\mu = \nabla_\lambda b + C_\lambda (2 \text{ in } g_{\alpha\beta},\ 1 \text{ in } u^\alpha,\ 0 \text{ in } h^\alpha).$$

Thus, the equation (44-1) can be written

$$\tfrac{1}{2}\,u^\alpha u^\beta \nabla_\alpha \nabla_\beta |\mathbf{h}|^2 + \tfrac{1}{2} u^\beta \nabla_\beta u^\alpha \nabla_\alpha |\mathbf{h}|^2 + |\mathbf{h}|^2 u^\beta \nabla_\beta a$$

$$+ a u^\beta \nabla_\beta |\mathbf{h}|^2 + u^\beta \nabla_\beta u^\mu (\tfrac{1}{2} \nabla_\mu |\mathbf{h}|^2$$

$$- u_\mu u^\alpha \nabla_\alpha |\mathbf{h}|^2) - h^\lambda \nabla_\lambda b$$

$$= D(2 \text{ in } g_{\alpha\beta},\ 1 \text{ in } f,\ 1 \text{ in } S,\ 1 \text{ in } u^\alpha,\ 0 \text{ in } h^\alpha). \tag{44-4}$$

But, according to (41-3), we have

$$\tfrac{1}{2}\, u^\beta \nabla_\beta |\mathbf{h}|^2 + a|\mathbf{h}|^2 + h^\lambda h^\mu \nabla_\lambda u_\mu = 0,$$

and so we obtain for (44-4), the form

$$\tfrac{1}{2}\, u^\alpha u^\beta \nabla_\alpha \nabla_\beta |\mathbf{h}|^2 + u^\beta \nabla_\beta u^\alpha \nabla_\alpha |\mathbf{h}|^2$$

$$+ |\mathbf{h}|^2 u^\beta \nabla_\beta a - h^\lambda \nabla_\lambda b$$

$$= E(2 \text{ in } g_{\alpha\beta},\ 1 \text{ in } f,\ 1 \text{ in } S,\ 1 \text{ in } u^\alpha,\ 0 \text{ in } h^\alpha),$$

without derivatives of h^α *in the right-hand side.*

(**b**) According to (41-5), we have

$$u^\beta \nabla_\beta a = -\frac{r'_f}{r} u^\alpha u^\beta \nabla_\alpha \nabla_\beta f$$

$$+ F(1 \text{ in } g_{\alpha\beta},\ 1 \text{ in } f,\ 1 \text{ in } S,\ 1 \text{ in } u^\alpha).$$

Moreover,

$$-h^\lambda \nabla_\lambda b = h^\beta \nabla_\beta \left(\frac{h^\alpha}{f} \nabla_\alpha f - \frac{T}{c^2 f} h^\alpha \nabla_\alpha S\right)$$

$$= \frac{h^\alpha h^\beta}{f}\left(\nabla_\alpha \nabla_\beta f - \frac{T}{c^2} \nabla_\alpha \nabla_\beta S\right)$$

$$+ G(1 \text{ in } g_{\alpha\beta},\ 1 \text{ in } f,\ 1 \text{ in } S,\ 0 \text{ in } h^\alpha)$$

$$+ \frac{h^\beta \nabla_\beta h^\alpha}{f}\left(\nabla_\alpha f - \frac{T}{c^2} \nabla_\alpha S\right).$$

We obtain thus for the equation (44-5) the other form

$$\tfrac{1}{2} u^\alpha u^\beta \nabla_\alpha \nabla_\beta |\mathbf{h}|^2 + u^\beta \nabla_\beta u^\alpha \nabla_\alpha |\mathbf{h}|^2$$

$$+ \left(\frac{h^\alpha h^\beta}{f} - |\mathbf{h}|^2 \frac{r'_f}{r} u^\alpha u^\beta\right) \nabla_\alpha \nabla_\beta f$$

$$- \frac{T}{c^2} \frac{h^\alpha h^\beta}{f} \nabla_\alpha \nabla_\beta S + \frac{h^\beta \nabla_\beta h^\alpha}{f}\left(\nabla_\alpha f - \frac{T}{c^2} \nabla_\alpha S\right)$$

$$= H(2 \text{ in } g_{\alpha\beta},\ 1 \text{ in } f,\ 1 \text{ in } S,\ 1 \text{ in } u^\alpha,\ 0 \text{ in } h^\alpha). \quad (44\text{-}5)$$

But,

$$u^\alpha u^\beta \nabla_\alpha \nabla_\beta S = u^\alpha \nabla_\alpha (u^\beta \nabla_\beta S) - u^\alpha \nabla_\alpha u^\beta \nabla_\beta S$$

$$= -u^\alpha \nabla_\alpha u^\beta \nabla_\beta S$$

and, therefore, (44-5) can be written

$$\tfrac{1}{2}\, u^\alpha u^\beta \nabla_\alpha \nabla_\beta\, |\mathbf{h}|^2 + u^\beta \nabla_\beta u^\alpha \nabla_\alpha\, |\mathbf{h}|^2$$
$$-\left(\frac{h^\alpha h^\beta}{f} - |\mathbf{h}|^2 \frac{r'_f}{r} u^\alpha u^\beta\right)\left(\nabla_\alpha \nabla_\beta f - \frac{T}{c^2}\nabla_\alpha \nabla_\beta S\right)$$
$$+ \frac{h^\beta \nabla_\beta h^\alpha}{f}\left(\nabla_\alpha f - \frac{T}{c^2}\nabla_\alpha S\right)$$
$$= I(2 \text{ in } g_{\alpha\beta},\ 1 \text{ in } f,\ 1 \text{ in } S,\ 1 \text{ in } u^\alpha,\ 0 \text{ in } h^\alpha). \qquad (44\text{-}6)$$

(**c**) Now, we multiply the two members of (44-6) by the operator $P^{\lambda\mu\nu\rho}\partial_{\lambda\mu\nu\rho}$, and we obtain

$$\tfrac{1}{2}\, P^{\lambda\mu\nu\rho}\partial_{\lambda\mu\nu\rho}(u^\alpha u^\beta \nabla_\alpha \nabla_\beta |\mathbf{h}|^2)$$
$$+ u^\beta \nabla_\beta u^\alpha \nabla_\alpha [P^{\lambda\mu\nu\rho}\partial_{\lambda\mu\nu\rho} |\mathbf{h}|^2]$$
$$+ P^{\lambda\mu\nu\rho}\partial_{\lambda\mu\nu\rho}(u^\beta \nabla_\beta u^\alpha)\nabla_\alpha |\mathbf{h}|^2$$
$$+ \left(\frac{h^\alpha h^\beta}{f} - |\mathbf{h}|^2 \frac{r'_f}{r} u^\alpha u^\beta\right)\nabla_\alpha \nabla_\beta$$
$$\times \left(P^{\lambda\mu\nu\rho}\partial_{\lambda\mu\nu\rho} f - \frac{T}{c^2} P^{\lambda\mu\nu\rho}\partial_{\lambda\mu\nu\rho} S\right)$$
$$+ P^{\lambda\mu\nu\rho}\partial_{\lambda\mu\nu\rho}\left(\frac{h^\alpha h^\beta}{f} - |\mathbf{h}|^2 \frac{r'_f}{r} u^\alpha u^\beta\right)$$
$$\times \left(\nabla_\alpha \nabla_\beta f - \frac{T}{c^2}\nabla_\alpha \nabla_\beta S\right) + P^{\lambda\mu\nu\rho}\partial_{\lambda\mu\nu\rho}$$
$$\times (h^\beta \nabla_\beta h^\alpha)\frac{1}{f}\left(\nabla_\alpha f - \frac{T}{c^2}\nabla_\alpha S\right) + \frac{h^\beta \nabla_\beta h^\alpha}{f}\nabla_\alpha$$
$$\times \left(P^{\lambda\mu\nu\rho}\partial_{\lambda\mu\nu\rho} f - \frac{T}{c^2} P^{\lambda\mu\nu\rho}\partial_{\lambda\mu\nu\rho} S\right)$$
$$= J(6 \text{ in } g_{\alpha\beta},\ 5 \text{ in } f,\ 5 \text{ in } |\mathbf{h}|^2,\ 5 \text{ in } S,\ 5 \text{ in } u^\alpha,\ 4 \text{ in } h^\alpha), \qquad (44\text{-}7)$$

that is,

$$\frac{1}{2} P^{\lambda\mu\nu\rho} \partial_{\lambda\mu\nu\rho} (u^\alpha u^\beta \nabla_\alpha \nabla_\beta |\mathbf{h}|^2$$

$$+ \left(\frac{h^\alpha h^\beta}{f} - |\mathbf{h}|^2 \frac{r'_f}{r} u^\alpha u^\beta\right) \nabla_\alpha \nabla_\beta$$

$$\times \left(P^{\lambda\mu\nu\rho} \partial_{\lambda\mu\nu\rho} f - \frac{T}{c^2} P^{\lambda\mu\nu\rho} \partial_{\lambda\mu\nu\rho} S\right)$$

$$+ P^{\lambda\mu\nu\rho} \partial_{\lambda\mu\nu\rho} (h^\alpha \nabla_\alpha h^\beta) \frac{1}{f} \left(\nabla_\beta f - \frac{T}{c^2} \nabla_\beta S\right)$$

$$= K(6 \text{ in } g_{\alpha\beta},\ 5 \text{ in } f,\ 5 \text{ in } |\mathbf{h}|^2,\ 5 \text{ in } S,\ 5 \text{ in } u^\alpha,\ 4 \text{ in } h^\alpha). \qquad (44\text{-}8)$$

But, according to (44-3), we have

$$h^\beta \nabla_\beta h^\alpha = -\tfrac{1}{2} g^{\alpha\beta} \nabla_\beta |\mathbf{h}|^2 + u^\alpha u^\beta \nabla_\beta |\mathbf{h}|^2$$
$$+ B^\alpha(1 \text{ in } g_{\alpha\beta},\ 1 \text{ in } f,\ 1 \text{ in } S,\ 1 \text{ in } u^\alpha,\ 0 \text{ in } h^\alpha),$$

that is,

$$h^\beta \nabla_\beta h^\alpha = L^\alpha(1 \text{ in } g_{\alpha\beta},\ 1 \text{ in } f,\ 1 \text{ in } |\mathbf{h}|^2,\ 1 \text{ in } S,\ 1 \text{ in } u^\alpha,\ 0 \text{ in } h^\alpha). \qquad (44\text{-}9)$$

It follows that

$$P^{\lambda\mu\nu\rho} \partial_{\lambda\mu\nu\rho} (h^\beta \nabla_\beta h^\alpha)$$
$$= M^\alpha(5 \text{ in } g_{\alpha\beta},\ 5 \text{ in } f,\ 5 \text{ in } |\mathbf{h}|^2,\ 5 \text{ in } S,\ 5 \text{ in } u^\alpha,\ 4 \text{ in } h^\alpha). \qquad (44\text{-}10)$$

If we use the equation (42-1) now, we see that

$$h^\alpha h^\beta \nabla_\alpha \nabla_\beta \left(P^{\lambda\mu\nu\rho}\partial_{\lambda\mu\nu\rho} f - \frac{T}{c^2} P^{\lambda\mu\nu\rho}\partial_{\lambda\mu\nu\rho} S\right)$$

$$= Y'(6 \text{ in } g_{\alpha\beta},\ 5 \text{ in f},\ 5 \text{ in S},\ 5 \text{ in } u^\alpha,\ 4 \text{ in } h^\beta \nabla_\beta h^\alpha)$$

and, according to (44-9), we have finally

$$h^\alpha h^\beta \nabla_\alpha \nabla_\beta \left(P^{\lambda\mu\nu\rho}\partial_{\lambda\mu\nu\rho} f - \frac{T}{c^2} P^{\lambda\mu\nu\rho}\partial_{\lambda\mu\nu\rho} S\right)$$

$$= Y(6 \text{ in } g_{\alpha\beta},\ 5 \text{ in f},\ 5 \text{ in } |\mathbf{h}|^2,\ 5 \text{ in S},\ 5 \text{ in } u^\alpha,\ 4 \text{ in } h^\alpha). \qquad (44\text{-}11)$$

Similarly, we have

$$u^\alpha u^\beta \nabla_\alpha \nabla_\beta \left(P^{\lambda\mu\nu\rho}\partial_{\lambda\mu\nu\rho} f - \frac{T}{c^2} P^{\lambda\mu\nu\rho}\partial_{\lambda\mu\nu\rho} S\right)$$

$$= Z'(6 \text{ in } g_{\alpha\beta},\ 5 \text{ in f},\ 5 \text{ in S},\ 5 \text{ in } u^\alpha,\ 4 \text{ in } u^\beta \nabla_\beta h^\alpha)$$

and, according to (44-2), we obtain

$$u^\alpha u^\beta \nabla_\alpha \nabla_\beta \left(p^{\lambda\mu\nu\rho}\partial_{\lambda\mu\nu\rho} f - \frac{T}{c^2} P^{\lambda\mu\nu\rho}\partial_{\lambda\mu\nu\rho} S\right)$$

$$= Z(6 \text{ in } g_{\alpha\beta},\ 5 \text{ in f},\ 5 \text{ in S},\ 5 \text{ in } u^\alpha,\ 4 \text{ in } h^\alpha). \qquad (44\text{-}12)$$

It follows from (44-10), (44-11), and (44-12) that the equation (44-8) can be written

$$\tfrac{1}{2} P^{\lambda\mu\nu\rho} \partial_{\lambda\mu\nu\rho} (u^\alpha u^\beta \nabla_\alpha \nabla_\beta |\mathbf{h}|^2)$$

$$= \tfrac{1}{2} X(6 \text{ in } g_{\alpha\beta},\ 5 \text{ in } f,\ 5 \text{ in } |\mathbf{h}|^2,$$

$$5 \text{ in } S,\ 5 \text{ in } u^\alpha,\ 4 \text{ in } h^\alpha),$$

and our lemma is proved.

45. System (III) of Magnetohydrodynamics

(**a**) Now, we are able to construct a differential system (III), which is a consequence of the system (II) and which is a Leray system. The unknowns here are $g_{\alpha\beta}$, f, $|h|^2$, S, u^α, h^α. We retain the Maxwell equations under the form (44-2), that is,

$$u^\rho \partial_\rho h^\tau = A^\tau (1 \text{ in } g_{\alpha\beta},\ 1 \text{ in } f,\ 1 \text{ in } S,\ 1 \text{ in } u^\alpha,\ 0 \text{ in } h^\alpha),$$

as well as the equation,

$$u^\rho \partial_\rho S = 0.$$

We consider the equations (42-1) and (42-2) corresponding to f and $|\mathbf{h}|^2$, and we take the derivative of these equations along the stream lines.
According to the above equations, we obtain

$$u^\rho P^{\alpha\beta\gamma\delta} \partial_{\alpha\beta\gamma\delta\rho} f = B(5 \text{ in } g_{\alpha\beta},\ 4 \text{ in } f,\ 4 \text{ in } S,$$

$$4 \text{ in } u^\alpha,\ 3 \text{ in } h^\alpha)$$

and also,

$$u^\rho P^{\alpha\beta\gamma\delta} \partial_{\alpha\beta\gamma\delta\rho} |\mathbf{h}|^2 = \subset (5 \text{ in } g_{\alpha\beta}, \ 4 \text{ in } f, \ 4 \text{ in } S,$$

$$4 \text{ in } u^\alpha, \ 3 \text{ in } h^\alpha).$$

We consider now the equations (43-5) concerning the u^τ and we multiply the two members by the operator $u^\rho P^{\alpha\beta\gamma\delta} \partial_{\alpha\beta\gamma\delta\rho}$. It follows, according to the above equations in f, in S and in h^τ, that

$$u^\rho P^{\alpha\beta\gamma\delta} Q^{\lambda\mu} \partial_{\alpha\beta\gamma\delta\lambda\mu\rho} u^\tau - \tfrac{1}{2}\mu g^{\sigma\tau} \nabla_\sigma$$

$$\times [P^{\alpha\beta\gamma\delta} \partial_{\alpha\beta\gamma\delta} (u^\lambda u^\mu \nabla_\lambda \nabla_\mu |\mathbf{h}|^2)]$$

$$= D^\tau (7 \text{ in } g_{\alpha\beta}, \ 6 \text{ in } f, \ 6 \text{ in } S, \ 6 \text{ in } u^\alpha, \ 5 \text{ in } h^\alpha).$$

But if we use our lemma, we obtain

$$u^\rho P^{\alpha\beta\gamma\delta} Q^{\lambda\mu} \partial_{\alpha\beta\gamma\delta\lambda\mu\rho} u^\tau = E^\tau (7 \text{ in } g_{\alpha\beta}, \ 6 \text{ in } f,$$

$$6 \text{ in } |h|^2, \ 6 \text{ in } S,$$

$$6 \text{ in } u^\alpha, \ 5 \text{ in } h^\alpha).$$

Finally, we substitute for the "Einstein equations" (35-12) of system (II) the derivatives along the stream lines, as in §16. According to our form of the Maxwell equations, we then obtain equations of the form

$$u^{\rho} g^{\alpha\beta} \partial_{\alpha\beta\rho} g_{\lambda\mu} = F_{\lambda\mu} (2 \text{ in } g_{\alpha\beta},\ 1 \text{ in } f,\ 1 \text{ in } S,$$

$$1 \text{ in } u^{\alpha},\ 0 \text{ in } h^{\alpha}).$$

(b) We have, thus, proved that each solution ($g_{\alpha\beta}$, f, $|\mathbf{h}|^2$, S, u^{α}, h^{α}) of the system (II) a is solution of a system (III) which is the set of the following equations:

$$u^{\rho} g^{\alpha\beta} \partial_{\alpha\beta\rho} g_{\lambda\mu} = F_{\lambda\mu} (2 \text{ in } g_{\alpha\beta},\ 1 \text{ in } f,\ 1 \text{ in } S,$$

$$1 \text{ in } u^{\alpha},\ 0 \text{ in } h^{\alpha}); \qquad (45\text{-}1)$$

the equations concerning f and $|\mathbf{h}|^2$:

$$u^{\rho} P^{\alpha\beta\gamma\delta} \partial_{\alpha\beta\gamma\delta\rho} f = B(5 \text{ in } g_{\alpha\beta},\ 4 \text{ in } f,\ 4 \text{ in } S,$$

$$4 \text{ in } u^{\alpha},\ 3 \text{ in } h^{\alpha}), \qquad (45\text{-}2)$$

$$u^{\rho} P^{\alpha\beta\gamma\delta} \partial_{\alpha\beta\gamma\delta\rho} |h|^2 = C(5 \text{ in } g_{\alpha\beta},\ 4 \text{ in } f,\ 4 \text{ in } S,$$

$$4 \text{ in } u^{\alpha},\ 3 \text{ in } h^{\alpha}); \qquad (45\text{-}3)$$

the equations concerning S:

$$u^{\rho} \partial_{\rho} S = 0; \qquad (45\text{-}4)$$

the system corresponding to u^{τ}:

$$u^\rho P^{\alpha\beta\gamma\delta} Q^{\lambda\mu} \partial_{\alpha\beta\gamma\delta\lambda\mu\rho} u^\tau = E^\tau (7 \text{ in } g_{\alpha\beta}, 6 \text{ in } f, 6 \text{ in } |\mathbf{h}|^2, 6 \text{ in } S, 6 \text{ in } u^\alpha, 5 \text{ in } h^\alpha); \tag{45-5}$$

and of the Maxwell equations:

$$u^\rho \partial_\rho h^\tau = A^\tau (1 \text{ in } g_{\alpha\beta}, 1 \text{ in } f, 1 \text{ in } S, 1 \text{ in } u^\alpha, 0 \text{ in } h^\alpha). \tag{45-6}$$

It is easy to see that this system (III) is a Leray system; the matrix A, here 21 × 21, is the matrix, whose diagonal elements are, respectively,

$$a(1) = u^\rho g^{\alpha\beta} \partial_{\alpha\beta\rho}, \ a(2) = a(3) = u^\rho P^{\alpha\beta\gamma\delta} \partial_{\alpha\beta\gamma\delta\rho},$$

$$a(4) = a(6) = u^\rho \partial_\rho, \ a(5) = u^\rho p^{\alpha\beta\gamma\delta} Q^{\lambda\mu} \partial_{\alpha\beta\gamma\delta\lambda\mu\rho}.$$

This system (III) satisfies the assumptions on the derivatives with the following indices for the unknowns:

$$s(g_{\alpha\beta}) = 8, \ s(f) = 7, \ s(|\mathbf{h}|^2) = 7, \ s(S) = 7,$$

$$s(u^\alpha) = 7, \ s(h^\alpha) = 6,$$

and the following indices for the equations:

$$t(1) = 6, \ t(2) = 3, \ t(3) = 3, \ t(4) = 7,$$

$$t(5) = 1, \ t(6) = 6.$$

Indeed a(1) has the order 3, a(2) = a(3) the order 5, a(4) = a(6) the order 1, a(5) the order 7. The table, giving for these indices the maximum order of derivation, is the following:

$$(1)\begin{cases} g_{\alpha\beta} : 2 \\ f : 1 \\ |\mathbf{h}|^2 : 1 \\ S : 1 \\ u^\alpha : 1 \\ h^\alpha : 0 \end{cases} \quad (2)\begin{cases} g_{\alpha\beta} : 5 \\ f : 4 \\ |\mathbf{h}|^2 : 4 \\ S : 4 \\ u^\alpha : 4 \\ h^\alpha : 3 \end{cases} \quad (3)\begin{cases} g_{\alpha\beta} : 5 \\ f : 4 \\ |\mathbf{h}|^2 : 4 \\ S : 4 \\ u^\alpha : 4 \\ h^\alpha : 3 \end{cases}$$

$$(4)\begin{cases} g_{\alpha\beta} : 1 \\ f : 0 \\ |\mathbf{h}|^2 : 0 \\ S : 0 \\ u^\alpha : 0 \\ h^\alpha : -1 \end{cases} \quad (5)\begin{cases} g_{\alpha\beta} : 7 \\ f : 6 \\ |\mathbf{h}|^2 : 6 \\ S : 6 \\ u^\alpha : 6 \\ h^\alpha : 5 \end{cases} \quad (6)\begin{cases} g_{\alpha\beta} : 2 \\ f : 1 \\ |\mathbf{h}|^2 : 1 \\ S : 1 \\ u^\alpha : 1 \\ h^\alpha : 0 \end{cases}$$

These maxima orders are compatible with our system (III). We have thus proved the following theorem.

Theorem. The system (III) of relativistic magnetohydrodynamics is a Leray system.

(**c**) On the regular hypersurface Σ, with the local equation $x^0 = 0$, we consider as initial data the values of the potentials $g_{\alpha\beta}$ and of their first derivatives, the values of the u_α defining a unitary vector and a convenient value of the total pressure defined by:

$$q = \frac{p}{c^2} + \tfrac{1}{2}\mu|\mathbf{h}|^2 .$$

We assume that these data are such that:

1. *The quadratic form* $g_{\lambda\mu} v^\lambda v^\mu$ *is normal hyperbolic; the hypersurface* Σ *is space-like at each point, with respect to the corresponding elementary cone.*

2. *We have on* Σ

$$F^\rho = 0, \qquad \text{for } x^0 = 0 .$$

3. *The relation* $S^0_\alpha = \chi T^0_\alpha$ *and the data give admissible values for* f, S *and the* h^α, *with*

$$\gamma = \frac{f r'_f}{r} \geq 1 .$$

The equations (35-12) of the system (II) give the values on Σ of the second derivatives of $g_{\alpha\beta}$; the equation (35-4) gives the values of the first derivatives of S. The equations (35-13), (35-14), (35-15) of the system (II) give, as we know, the first derivatives of f, u^α, and h^α. By differentiation of these equations, we obtain the values of the second derivatives of f, S, u^α, and h^α. The equations (45-1) and their derivatives give the values of the derivative of $g_{\alpha\beta}$ of order $\leq$ 4. By differentiation of (35-13), (35-14), (35-15), and of (45-1) and (45-4), we are thus able to find on Σ the derivatives of $g_{\alpha\beta}$ of order $\leq$ 7, the derivatives of f, S, u^α of order $\leq$ 6, and the derivatives of h^α of order $\leq$ 5. If we differentiate (45-3), we have on Σ the derivatives of $|\mathbf{h}|^2$ of order $\leq$ 6.

We have thus obtained the values on Σ of the derivatives of the unknowns of order $\leq s(\sigma) - 1$, that is, we have obtained *a Cauchy problem for the system* (III).

(d) We assume, in the following part, that we are in the general case where

$$\gamma = \frac{f r'_f}{r} \neq \frac{rf + \mu |h|^2}{\mu |\mathbf{h}|^2} . \qquad (45\text{-}7)$$

According to the study of §40, we know that under our assumptions the operators $a(1)$ and $a(4) = a(6)$ are, of course, strictly hyperbolic, that the operator $a(2) = a(3)$ is the product of *two* strictly hyperbolic operators, and that the operator $a(5)$ is the product of *four* strictly hyperbolic operators ($p = 4$). Let us consider now a convenient domain $Y(0 \leq |x^0| \leq C)$ in the neighborhood of Σ. An integer $q \geq 0$ and a real $\alpha \geq 1$ being given, we denote by $\gamma_q^{(\alpha)}(Y)$ the corresponding Gevrey class (Leray and Ohya [6]) on the domain Y and by $\gamma_q^{s(\alpha)}(Y)$ the class of the functions such that their derivatives of order $\leq s$ are contained in the Gevrey class $\gamma_q^{(\alpha)}(Y)$. It is well known that $\gamma_\infty^{s(\alpha)}(Y)$ is an algebra and that $\gamma_q^{s,(\alpha)}$ is a modulus onto this algebra. If $\alpha = 1$, these classes are classes of analytic functions; but if $\alpha > 1$, we have classes of *no quasi-analytic functions*: these classes contain functions with a compact support.

It follows from a theorem of Leray and Ohya [6], completed by Leray, that we have here the following result: we see that, in our system (III), we have at most in the left members the product of $p = 4$ strictly hyperbolic operators; therefore, we consider the numbers α such that $1 \leq \alpha \leq p/p - 1 = 4/3$. *The Cauchy problem of the system (III) has then one and only one solution in a class* $\gamma_2^{(\sigma)+6,(\alpha)}(Y)$, where $1 \leq \alpha \leq 4/3$ and where Y is convenient.

The same argument as in §15 shows that this solution of (III) is a solution of the system (II), and, according to the choice of our initial data, is a solution of the main system (I).

We have thus proved that *the Cauchy problem for the main system of the relativistic magnetohydrodynamics has an existence and uniqueness theorem in convenient Gevrey classes.*

Chapter 5

SHOCK WAVES IN MAGNETOHYDRODYNAMICS

In this chapter, we shall extend the considerations of Chapter 4 to include shock waves. We first define the notion of a shock wave, and show that shock waves are naturally divided into two types: tangential and nontangential shocks. It is seen that the shock wave phenomenon bears a close relation to the Alfven and hydrodynamical waves discussed in Chapter IV. We then show that, in the classical limit, the relativistic treatment of shock waves goes over into the well-known classical treatment.

46. The Main System

(**a**) We change h_α to h_α/c^2 in order to come back to the usual units. We consider thus the following energy tensor

$$T_{\alpha\beta} = (c^2 rf + \mu|h|^2)\, u_\alpha u_\beta - q g_{\alpha\beta} - \mu h_\alpha h_\beta , \tag{46-1}$$

where

$$q = p + \tfrac{1}{2}\mu\, |h|^2 . \tag{46-2}$$

The space-time V_4 is here a given background. The results of the following study are thus available in the frames of special relativity and of general relativity. The main system of magnetohydrodynamics is then

$$\nabla_\alpha (ru^\alpha) = 0 , \tag{46-3}$$

$$\nabla_\alpha (u^\alpha h^\beta - u^\beta h^\alpha) = 0, \tag{46-4}$$

$$\nabla_\alpha T^{\alpha\beta} = 0. \tag{46-5}$$

(**b**) The characteristic manifolds of the previous system are the hypersurfaces generated by the stream lines and 1° the *hydrodynamical waves*, solutions of (35-27) with

$$P^{\lambda\mu\nu\rho} = c^2 rf (\gamma - 1) u^\lambda u^\mu u^\nu u^\rho + (c^2 rf + \mu |h|^2 \gamma) \times g^{(\lambda\mu} u^\nu u^{\rho)} - \mu g^{(\lambda\mu} h^\nu h^{\rho)}; \tag{46-6}$$

2° the *Alfven waves*, solutions of

$$(c^2 rf + \mu |h|^2)(u^\alpha \partial_\alpha \varphi)^2 - \mu (h^\alpha \partial_\alpha \varphi)^2 = 0. \tag{46-7}$$

The Alfven waves play an important part in the theory of the shock waves.

47. Shock Equations

(**a**) We suppose, in the following part, that the $g_{\alpha\beta}$ and their first derivatives are continuous. A shock wave is a time-like hypersurface Σ of V_4 across which u^α, h^α or one of the thermodynamical variables are discontinuous.

If $\varphi = 0$ is the local equation of Σ, $\partial_\alpha \varphi$ defines a vector orthogonal to Σ. Let n_α be the normalized vector ($n^\alpha n_\alpha = -1$) collinear to $\partial_\alpha \varphi$. We are led to decompose the magnetic field according to a tangential component and a normal component with respect to Σ. We let

$$h^\alpha = t^\alpha - \eta n^\alpha, \qquad t^\alpha n_\alpha = 0, \tag{47-1}$$

where t^{α} is the tangential magnetic field and where

$$\eta = h^{\alpha} n_{\alpha} . \tag{47-2}$$

It follows from (47-1) that t^{α} is space-like with

$$|t|^2 = -t^{\alpha} t_{\alpha} = |h|^2 - \eta^2 \geq 0 . \tag{47-3}$$

(**b**) Let Q′ (or Q) be the value of a quantity after (before) the shock; [Q] is here the discontinuity Q′ − Q of the considered quantity in a point of Σ.

The main system (46-3), (46-4), (46-5) is to be satisfied in the sense of distributions. It follows, by a classical argument, that the singular measures supported by Σ and defined by the derivations vanish[1]. We deduce thus from the main system the shock equations:

$$[ru^{\alpha}] n_{\alpha} = 0, \tag{47-4}$$

$$[h^{\alpha} u^{\beta} - u^{\alpha} h^{\beta}] n_{\alpha} = 0, \tag{47-5}$$

$$[T^{\alpha\beta}] n_{\alpha} = 0. \tag{47-6}$$

From (47-4) follows the invariance of the scalar

$$a = ru^{\alpha} n_{\alpha} , \tag{47-7}$$

and from (47-5) the invariance of the vector

$$V^{\beta} = \eta u^{\beta} - \frac{a}{r} h^{\beta} , \tag{47-8}$$

---

[1] See, for example, L. Schwartz, Théorie des distributions, t. 1, 43-44.

where η is defined by (47-2). We remark that

$$V^{\beta} n_{\beta} = \eta u^{\beta} n_{\beta} - \frac{a}{r}\eta = \frac{a}{r}\eta - \frac{a}{r}\eta = 0 .$$

It follows that *the invariant vector* V^{β} *is tangent to the shock wave* Σ.

According to the formula (46-1) giving the energy tensor, we deduce from (46-6) that the vector

$$W^{\beta} = a\left(c^2 \frac{f}{r} + \mu \frac{|h|^2}{r^2}\right) ru^{\beta} - q n^{\beta} - \mu \eta h^{\beta} ,$$

$$r,\ r' > 0 \tag{47-9}$$

is invariant across Σ. We always suppose, in the following part, that $r > 0$, $r' > 0$.

From the invariance of

$$a = ru^{\alpha} n_{\alpha} = r' u'^{\alpha} n_{\alpha} ,$$

it follows that $u^{\alpha} n_{\alpha} = 0$ if and only if $u'^{\alpha} n_{\alpha} = 0$ (tangential shocks). For a nontangential shock, $u^{\alpha} n_{\alpha}$ and $u'^{\alpha} n_{\alpha}$ have, of course, the same sign (here the sign $-$).

48. Tangential Shocks

Let us consider the case of the tangential shocks $a = 0$. We have

$$u^{\alpha} n_{\alpha} = u'^{\alpha} n_{\alpha} = 0 . \tag{48-1}$$

It follows from (47-8) and (47-9),

$$\eta u^{\beta} = \eta' u'^{\beta} , \tag{48-2}$$

$$(q' - q) n^{\beta} + \mu (\eta' h'^{\beta} - \eta h^{\beta}) = 0 . \tag{48-3}$$

We are led to consider tangential shocks of two types:

(a) type I: $\eta \neq 0$. We see that the vectors u^β and u'^β are unitary and collinear. Thus $u'^\beta = \pm u^\beta$. But the sign $-$ is not compatible with the orientation of the velocity vectors toward the future. It follows that $[u^\beta] = 0$ and $[\eta] = 0$. We have thus

$$[u^\beta] = 0, \qquad [h^\beta] = 0, \qquad [p] = 0, \tag{48-4}$$

and the discontinuity of r is undetermined.

(b) type II: $\eta = 0$. We deduce from (48-2) that $\eta' = 0$ and the general shock equations give only

$$u^\alpha n_\alpha = u'^\alpha n_\alpha = 0, \qquad h^\alpha n_\alpha = h'^\alpha n_\alpha = 0,$$

$$[p + \tfrac{1}{2}\mu\, |h|^2] = 0. \tag{48-5}$$

The other discontinuities are undetermined.

49. Invariants of the Nontangetial Shocks

We suppose hereafter $a \neq 0$ (nontangential shock), and we introduce the invariant scalar defined by

$$H = \frac{1}{a^2} V^\beta V_\beta = \frac{\eta^2}{a^2} - \frac{|h|^2}{r^2}. \tag{49-1}$$

H is positive if and only if V^β is *time-like*.

(a) First, we seek a convenient expression of the invariant vector W^β. We deduce from (47-8),

$$h^\beta = \frac{\eta}{a} r u^\beta - \frac{r}{a} V^\beta,$$

and so we obtain from (47-9),

$$W^\beta = a\left(c^2 \frac{f}{r} + \mu \frac{|h|^2}{r^2}\right) ru^\beta - qh^\beta - \mu \frac{\eta^2}{a} ru^\beta$$

$$+ \mu \frac{r\eta}{a} V^\beta ,$$

or,

$$W^\beta = a\left(c^2 \frac{f}{r} - \mu H\right) ru^\beta - qn^\beta + \mu \frac{r\eta}{a} V^\beta .$$

If we introduce the variable

$$\alpha = c^2 \frac{f}{r} - \mu H , \tag{49-2}$$

we have

$$W^\beta = a\alpha ru^\beta - qn^\beta + \mu \frac{r\eta}{a} V^\beta . \tag{49-3}$$

Let us decompose ru^β according to a tangential component and a normal component with respect to Σ. We obtain

$$ru^\beta = w^\beta - an^\beta , \qquad w^\beta n_\beta = 0 \tag{49-4}$$

and thus

$$w^\beta = ru^\beta + n^\beta . \tag{49-5}$$

From (49-3) and (49-4) we deduce

$$W^\beta = X^\beta - (q + a^2\alpha) n^\beta , \tag{49-6}$$

where

$$X^\beta = a\alpha w^\beta + \mu \frac{r\eta}{a} V^\beta \tag{49-7}$$

is tangent to Σ. The vector W^{β} being invariant through the shock, it is the same for its tangential part and for its normal part. Thus the vector X^{β} and the scalar $(q + a^2\alpha)$ are invariant.

According to (49-3), the invariant scalar $X^{\beta} V_{\beta}$ can be written

$$X^{\beta} V_{\beta} = W^{\beta} V_{\beta} = ar\eta(\alpha + \mu H),$$

that is, according to (49-2),

$$X^{\beta} V_{\beta} = c^2 af\eta . \tag{49-8}$$

We are led thus to introduce the two invariant scalars:

$$b = f\eta, \qquad l = \alpha + \frac{q}{a^2} .$$

(b) Let us consider now the invariant scalar

$$K = \frac{1}{a^2} X^{\beta} X_{\beta} .$$

From (49-5), it follows that

$$w^{\beta} w_{\beta} = r^2 + a^2, \qquad w^{\beta} V_{\beta} = ru^{\beta} V_{\beta} = r\eta . \tag{49-9}$$

We thus obtain from (49-7),

$$K = (r^2 + a^2)\alpha^2 + 2\mu \frac{r^2\eta^2}{a^2} \alpha + \mu \frac{r^2\eta^2}{a^2} H. \tag{49-10}$$

If we substitute for α the value (49-2), we have

$$K = c^4(r^2 + a^2)\frac{f^2}{r^2} + 2\mu c^2 \frac{f}{r}\left\{\frac{r^2\eta^2}{a^2} - (r^2 + a^2)H\right\}$$

$$- \mu^2 H\left\{\frac{r^2\eta^2}{a^2} - (r^2 + a^2)H\right\},$$

but, according to the definition of H,

$$\frac{r^2\eta^2}{a^2} - (r^2 + a^2)H = \frac{r^2\eta^2}{a^2} - r^2\left(\frac{\eta^2}{a^2} - \frac{|h|^2}{r^2}\right) - a^2 H$$

$$= |h|^2 - a^2 H .$$

In the following part, we let

$$k^2 = \frac{r^2\eta^2}{a^2} - (r^2 + a^2)H = |h|^2 - a^2 H$$

$$= |t|^2 + \frac{a^2}{r^2}|h|^2, \qquad (49\text{-}11)$$

where k^2 *is strictly positive for a non-vanishing magnetic field.*

We obtain thus the invariant scalar:

$$K = c^4(r^2 + a^2)\frac{f^2}{r^2} + 2\mu c^2 \frac{f}{r} k^2 - \mu^2 H k^2 . \qquad (49\text{-}12)$$

(**c**) Let us transform the expression of HK, where K is given by (49-10). From

$$HK = H(r^2 + a^2)\alpha^2 + \frac{r^2\eta^2}{a^2}\mu H(2\alpha + \mu H),$$

where $\mu H = c^2 f/r - \alpha$, it follows that

$$HK = H(r^2 + a^2)\alpha^2 + \frac{r^2\eta^2}{a^2}\left(c^2\frac{f}{r} - \alpha\right)\left(c^2\frac{f}{r} + \alpha\right),$$

that is,

$$HK = H(r^2 + a^2)\alpha^2 + \frac{r^2\eta^2}{a^2}\left(c^4\frac{f^2}{r^2} - \alpha^2\right).$$

We thus obtain

$$HK = \left\{H(r^2 + a^2) - \frac{r^2\eta^2}{a^2}\right\}\alpha^2 + c^4\frac{f^2\eta^2}{a^2},$$

where the term $c^4 b^2/a^2$ is invariant. Therefore, we are led to consider the invariant scalar:

$$L = c^4\frac{b^2}{a^2} - HK,$$

which can be written

$$L = \left\{\frac{r^2\eta^2}{a^2} - (r^2 + a^2)H\right\}\alpha^2 \tag{49-13}$$

or

$$L = k^2\alpha^2. \tag{49-14}$$

50. Analysis of a Nontangential Shock

(a) From previous study, it follows that the two thermodynamical variables and the three scalars $u^\alpha n_\alpha$, $h^\alpha n_\alpha$, $|h|^2$ satisfy the five relations:

$$a = ru^\alpha n_\alpha = r'u'^\alpha n_\alpha, \tag{50-1}$$

$$b = f\eta = f'\eta', \tag{50-2}$$

$$H = \frac{\eta^2}{a^2} - \frac{|h|^2}{r^2} = \frac{\eta'^2}{a^2} - \frac{|h'|^2}{r'^2}, \tag{50-3}$$

$$1 = \alpha + \frac{q}{a^2} = \alpha' + \frac{q'}{a^2}, \tag{50-4}$$

$$K = c^4 (r^2 + a^2) \frac{f^2}{r^2} + 2\mu c^2 k^2 \frac{f}{r} - \mu^2 H k^2$$

$$= c^4 (r'^2 + a^2) \frac{f'^2}{r'^2} + 2\mu c^2 k'^2 \frac{f'}{r'} - \mu^2 H k'^2, \tag{50-5}$$

where k^2 is defined by (49-11).

From (50-2) and (50-3), it follows that *the magnetic field vanishes after (before) the shock if and only if it vanishes before (after) the shock.*

(b) Let r', f', $u'^{\alpha} n_{\alpha}$, $\eta' = h'^{\alpha} n_{\alpha}$, $|h'|$ be a solution of the previous equations. At the point x of Σ, we introduce for a moment an orthonormalized frame $\{e_{(\alpha)}\}$ such that $e_{(1)}$ coincides with n. With respect to this frame, the general shock equations (47-5) and (47-6) give

$$\begin{cases} h'^1 u'^i - u'^1 h'^i = h^1 u^i - u^1 h^i, \\ (c^2 r' f' + \mu |h'|^2) u'^1 u'^i - \mu h'^1 h'^i \\ \qquad = (c^2 rf + \mu |h|^2) u^1 u^i - \mu h^1 h^i, \end{cases} \tag{50-6}$$

where $i = 0, 2, 3$ and where $u'^1 = -u'^{\alpha} n_{\alpha}$, $h'^1 = -h'^{\alpha} n_{\alpha}$. Let us consider the determinant of the left-hand side, with respect to the unknowns u'^i, h'^i:

$$D' = (c^2 r' f' + \mu |h'|^2)(u'^{\alpha} n_{\alpha})^2 - \mu (h'^{\alpha} n_{\alpha})^2.$$

If $D' \neq 0$, the equations (50-6) determine u'^i and h'^i. Among the relations (50-1), ..., (50-5), the relation (50-1) is one from the general shock equations and the relation (50-4) expresses the invariance of the normal component of W^β. The relations (50-2), (50-3), (50-5) are consequences of (50-1), (50-4), and (50-6) and play the part of compatibility conditions.

According to (46-7), the relation $D' = 0$ expresses that Σ is an Alfven wave after the shock. Let us consider the scalar

$$D = (c^2 rf + \mu |h|^2)(u^\alpha n_\alpha)^2 - \mu (h^\alpha n_\alpha)^2$$
$$= \left(c^2 \frac{f}{r} + \mu \frac{|h|^2}{r^2}\right) a^2 - \mu \eta^2 .$$

It follows that

$$\frac{D}{a^2} = c^2 \frac{f}{r} + \mu \frac{|h|^2}{r^2} - \mu \frac{\eta^2}{a^2} = c^2 \frac{f}{r} - \mu H = \alpha .$$

Thus

$$\frac{D}{a^2} = \alpha , \qquad \frac{D'}{a^2} = \alpha' , \tag{50-7}$$

and we see the interpretation of the variable α in terms of the Alfven wave operator.

(c) According to (49-14), we have

$$k^2 \alpha^2 = k'^2 \alpha'^2 , \tag{50-8}$$

where k^2 and k'^2 are strictly positive for a nonvanishing magnetic field. With convenient signs for k and k', (50-8) can be written

$$k\alpha = k' \alpha' . \tag{50-9}$$

Let us suppose that Σ is an Alfven wave after the shock ($\alpha' = 0$). We have necessarily $H > 0$. The magnetic field h'^β and, thus (cf. section (a)), the magnetic field h^β are different from zero in $x \in \Sigma$; k^2 is therefore > 0. From (50-8), it follows that $\alpha = 0$ and Σ is an Alfven wave before the shock. We obtain the following theorem.

Theorem. In a nontangential shock, the shock wave Σ *is an Alfven wave after the shock if and only if* Σ *is an Alfven wave before the shock.*

If such is the case, that is, if $\alpha' = \alpha = 0$, the shock is called an Alfven shock. We will study these shocks in the following section.

(d) The following lemma will help us.

Lemma. The invariant K *can be written*

$$K = c^4 f^2 + \mu |h|^2 c^2 \frac{f}{r} + \mu |h|^2 \alpha + a^2 \alpha^2 . \qquad (50\text{-}10)$$

According to (50-5), we have

$$K = c^4 f^2 + a^2 c^4 \frac{f^2}{r^2} + 2\mu c^2 \frac{f}{r}(|h|^2 - a^2 H)$$

$$- \mu^2 H(|h|^2 - a^2 H)$$

or

$$K = c^4 f^2 + \mu |h|^2 \left(2c^2 \frac{f}{r} - \mu H\right)$$

$$+ a^2 \left(c^4 \frac{f^2}{r^2} - 2c^2 \frac{f}{r} \mu H + \mu^2 H^2\right),$$

that is,

$$K = c^4 f^2 + \mu |h|^2 c^2 \frac{f}{r} + \mu |h|^2 \alpha + a^2 \alpha^2 ,$$

and the formula (50-10) is proved.

Let us suppose now that $\alpha' = \alpha \neq 0$. We have

$$\left[\frac{f}{r}\right] = 0. \tag{50-11}$$

Under our assumption, it follows from (50-8) that $k'^2 = k^2$; according to (49-11), we then have

$$[\,|h|^2] = 0. \tag{50-12}$$

From (50-4), it follows that $[q] = 0$ and thus

$$[p] = 0. \tag{50-13}$$

In K given by (50-10), the three last terms are invariant in the shock. We obtain, therefore,

$$[f] = 0,$$

and, according to (50-11),

$$[r] = 0.$$

Thus, it follows from (50-1), (50-2) that

$$[u^\alpha n_\alpha] = 0, \qquad [h^\alpha n_\alpha] = 0.$$

Σ being a non-Alfven wave, we deducc from (50-6) that u^α, h^α and the thermodynamical variables are continuous across Σ.

Theorem. If $\alpha' = \alpha \neq 0$, *then the shock vanishes.*

51. Analysis of the Alfven Shocks

(a) If we consider f and S as the main thermodynamical variables, we know that the velocity v_0 of the hydrodynamical waves is given by

$$\gamma = \frac{fr'f}{r} = \frac{c^2}{v_0^2}.$$

We suppose here that $v_0 < c$, that is,

$$fr'f - r > 0. \tag{51-1}$$

Under this assumption we will study the Alfven shocks. According to §50, we have

$$c^2 \frac{f}{r} = c^2 \frac{f'}{r'} = \mu H \tag{51-2}$$

and thus

$$\left[\frac{f}{r}\right] = 0. \tag{51-3}$$

From the relations (50-1) , . . . , (50-4) it follows that

$$[ru^\alpha n_\alpha] = 0, \qquad [f\eta] = 0, \quad \left[\frac{\eta^2}{a^2} - \frac{|h|^2}{r^2}\right] = 0,$$

$$[p + \tfrac{1}{2}\mu|h|^2] = 0. \tag{51-4}$$

According to (50-10), the invariance of K gives

$$\left[c^2 f^2 + \mu |h|^2 \frac{f}{r}\right] = 0,$$

that is, according to (51-3),

$$[c^2 rf + \mu|h|^2] = 0.$$

But $\mu|h|^2 = -[2p]$. We thus obtain

$$[c^2 rf - 2p] = 0. \tag{51-5}$$

(**b**) We study now the independence of the two thermodynamical variables:

$$\varphi = c^2 rf - 2p, \qquad \psi = \log(f/r)$$

considered as functions of f and S. According to (33-3),

$$dp = c^2 r \, df - rT \, dS .$$

By differentiation of φ and ψ with respect to f and S, we have

$$\varphi'_f = c^2 (f r'_f - r), \qquad \psi'_f = -\frac{f r'_f - r}{rf}$$

$$\varphi'_S = c^2 f r'_S + 2rT, \qquad \psi'_S = -\frac{r'_S}{r} .$$

The corresponding Jacobian is

$$\frac{d(\varphi, \psi)}{d(f, S)} = (f r'_f - r) \left(-c^2 \frac{r'_S}{r} + c^2 \frac{r'_S}{r} + 2 \frac{T}{f} \right),$$

that is,

$$\frac{d(\varphi, \psi)}{d(f, S)} = 2 \frac{T}{f} (f r'_f - r) \neq 0 .$$

Under our assumption, the variables φ and ψ are independent and are continuous through Σ according to (51-3) and (51-5); f and S are thus continuous through Σ and we have

$$[r] = 0, \qquad [f] = 0, \qquad [p] = 0. \tag{51-6}$$

From (51-4), it follows that

$$[u^\alpha n_\alpha] = 0, \qquad [h^\alpha n_\alpha] = 0, \qquad [|h|^2] = 0. \tag{51-7}$$

The direction of the tangential magnetic field after the shock is undetermined. The tangential velocity of the fluid after the shock is connected to the tangential magnetic field by the relations (50-6). We thus have

$$\left(c^2 \frac{f}{r} + \mu \frac{|h|^2}{r^2}\right) ru^\alpha n_\alpha [w^\beta] - \mu\eta[t^\beta] = 0 .$$

(**c**) In the following part we set

$$\beta = \left\{\frac{c^2 rf + \mu|h|^2}{\mu}\right\}^{\frac{1}{2}} . \tag{51-8}$$

Equation (46-7) can be written

$$\beta^2 (u^\alpha \partial_\alpha \varphi)^2 - (h^\alpha \partial_\alpha \varphi)^2$$

$$= \{\beta u^\alpha \partial_\alpha \varphi + h^\alpha \partial_\alpha \varphi\} \{\beta u^\alpha \partial_\alpha \varphi - h^\alpha \partial_\alpha \varphi\} = 0 ,$$

and the Alfven waves can be decomposed in two kinds, called A-waves and B-waves, satisfying, respectively,

$$\text{(A)} \quad (\beta u^\alpha + h^\alpha)\partial_\alpha \varphi = 0; \qquad \text{(B)} \quad (\beta u^\alpha - h^\alpha)\partial_\alpha \varphi = 0.$$

Thus, the Alfven waves are generated by the trajectories either of the vector field

$$A^\alpha = \beta u^\alpha + h^\alpha \tag{51-9}$$

or of the vector field

$$B^\alpha = \beta u^\alpha - h^\alpha . \tag{51-10}$$

β being positive, the vectors A^α and B^α are time-like and oriented toward the future.

Let us study, in an Alfven shock, the vectors A^α and B^α. If we introduce for a moment the orthonormalized frame of §50(b), we have, according to (50-6),

$$\beta^2 u^\alpha n_\alpha [u^i] - h^\alpha n_\alpha [h^i] = 0, \qquad i = 0, 2, 3. \tag{51-11}$$

If the shock is an Alfven shock of the kind A, that is, if Σ is generated by trajectories of A:

$$A^\alpha n_\alpha = \beta u^\alpha n_\alpha + h^\alpha n_\alpha = 0,$$

and (51-11) can be written

$$\beta u^\alpha n_\alpha [\beta u^i + h^i] = 0.$$

It follows since the shock is nontangential that

$$[\beta u^i + h^i] = [A^i] = 0.$$

A^1 being invariant in an Alfven shock, we obtain

$$[A^\alpha] = 0. \tag{51-12}$$

Thus

Theorem. For an Alfven shock of the kind A (or B) the vector A^α (or B^α) *is invariant in the shock.*

52. The Vector U^β for a Nontangential Shock

We consider now a nontangential shock which is not an Alfven shock ($a\alpha \neq 0$) and for which V^β is not isotropic ($H \neq 0$).

(**a**) We have

$$V^\beta = \frac{\eta}{r} w^\beta - \frac{a}{r} t^\beta. \tag{52-1}$$

According to (49-9), w^β is time-like and different from zero, the vector t^β is space-like, and we have

$$t^\beta V_\beta = h^\beta V_\beta = \frac{a}{r} |h|^2 .$$

If we suppose $h^\beta \neq 0$, we have $t^\beta \neq 0$ and *the vector* V^β *is not collinear to* w^β.

According to (49-7), X^β is in the 2-plane in $x \in \Sigma$ defined by V^β and w^β; α being $\neq 0$, this 2-plane can be defined by the vectors V^β and X^β and is invariant in the shock. Let Π_x be this 2-plane.

Thus the tangential components of the velocity and of the magnetic field in $x \in \Sigma$ *are in a 2-plane* Π_x *invariant in the shock.*

(**b**) Let us consider, in Π_x, the vector U^β defined by

$$\alpha U^\beta = \frac{H}{a} X^\beta . \tag{52-2}$$

The vector αU^β is invariant in the shock and orthogonal to V^β, according to (49-8):

$$\alpha U^\beta V_\beta = \frac{H}{a} X^\beta V_\beta - c^2 bH = c^2 (bH - bH) = 0 .$$

It follows from (49-7) that

$$\alpha U^\beta = \frac{H}{a}\left(a\alpha w^\beta + \mu \frac{r\eta}{a} V^\beta \right) - c^2 \frac{f\eta}{a^2} V^\beta ,$$

that is,

$$\alpha U^\beta = \alpha H w^\beta - \frac{r\eta}{a^2}\left(c^2 \frac{f}{r} - \mu H \right) V^\beta .$$

We thus obtain

$$U^{\beta} = Hw^{\beta} - \frac{r\eta}{a^2} V^{\beta} \tag{52-3}$$

or

$$U^{\beta} = \frac{\eta}{a} t^{\beta} + \left(H - \frac{\eta^2}{a^2}\right) w^{\beta},$$

that is,

$$U^{\beta} = \frac{\eta}{a} t^{\beta} - \frac{|h|^2}{r^2} w^{\beta}. \tag{52-4}$$

According to (52-2), we have

$$\alpha^2 U^{\beta} U_{\beta} = H^2 K + c^4 \frac{b^2}{a^2} H - 2c^4 \frac{b^2}{a^2} H$$

$$= H^2 K - c^4 \frac{b^2}{a^2} H.$$

From the expression of L, it follows that

$$\alpha^2 U^{\beta} U_{\beta} = -HL.$$

We thus obtain

$$U^{\beta} U_{\beta} = -Hk^2. \tag{52-5}$$

(c) U^{β} being collinear to itself in the shock, we have, according to (50-9),

$$U'^{\beta} = \frac{\alpha}{\alpha'} U^{\beta} = \frac{k'}{k} U^{\beta}.$$

It follows that

$$[U^{\beta}] = \left(\frac{k'}{k} - 1\right) U^{\beta}$$

and

$$[U^\beta][U_\beta] = \left(\frac{k'}{k} - 1\right)^2 U^\beta U_\beta = -H(k' - k)^2 . \tag{52-6}$$

If $|[U]|^2$ is the absolute value of the left-hand side of (52-6), we have

$$(k' - k)^2 = \frac{|[U]|^2}{|H|} . \tag{52-7}$$

53. Relativistic Hugoniot Equation

It is possible to write the equation (50-5) in a form which gives the relativistic generalization of the classical Hugoniot equation for the magnetohydrodynamics.

(a) (50-5) can be written

$$c^4 [f^2] + c^4 a^2 \left[\frac{f^2}{r^2}\right] + 2\mu c^2 \left[\frac{f}{r} k^2\right] - \mu^2 H[k^2] = 0 . \tag{53-1}$$

Let us study the term

$$c^4 a^2 \left[\frac{f^2}{r^2}\right] = c^2 \left(\frac{f'}{r'} + \frac{f}{r}\right) a^2 \left(c^2 \frac{f'}{r'} - c^2 \frac{f}{r}\right)$$

$$= c^2 \left(\frac{f'}{r'} + \frac{f}{r}\right) a^2 [\alpha] .$$

From (50-4), it follows that

$$a^2[\alpha] = -[p] - \tfrac{1}{2}\mu[|h|^2] .$$

But $[k^2] = [|h|^2]$, and so it follows that

$$c^4 a^2 \left[\frac{f^2}{r^2}\right] = -c^2\left(\frac{f}{r} + \frac{f'}{r'}\right)[p] - \frac{1}{2}\mu c^2\left(\frac{f}{r} + \frac{f'}{r'}\right)[k^2].$$

Thus the relation (53-1) can be written

$$c^4[f^2] - c^2\left(\frac{f}{r} + \frac{f'}{r'}\right)[p] - \frac{1}{2}\mu c^2\left(\frac{f}{r} + \frac{f'}{r'}\right)[k^2]$$
$$+ 2\mu c^2\left[\frac{f}{r}\,k^2\right] - \mu^2 H[k^2] = 0. \qquad (53\text{-}2)$$

We consider now the term

$$\left[\frac{f}{r}\,k^2\right] = \frac{f'}{r'}\,k'^2 - \frac{f}{r}\,k^2;$$

we have

$$\left[\frac{f}{r}\,k^2\right] = \frac{f'}{r'}\,(k'^2 - k^2) + \left(\frac{f'}{r'} - \frac{f}{r}\right)k^2$$

and also

$$\left[\frac{f}{r}\,k^2\right] = \left(\frac{f'}{r'} - \frac{f}{r}\right)k'^2 + \frac{f}{r}\,(k'^2 - k^2);$$

we obtain thus

$$2\left[\frac{f}{r}\,k^2\right] = \left[\frac{f}{r}\right](k^2 + k'^2) + \left(\frac{f}{r} + \frac{f'}{r'}\right)[k^2],$$

and so the relation (53-2) can be written

$$c^4[f^2] - c^2\left(\frac{f}{r} + \frac{f'}{r'}\right)[p] + \frac{1}{2}\mu\left(c^2\frac{f}{r} + c^2\frac{f'}{r'} - 2\mu H\right)$$
$$\times [k^2] + \mu c^2\left[\frac{f}{r}\right](k^2 + k'^2) = 0,$$

that is,

$$c^4[f^2] - c^2\left(\frac{f}{r} + \frac{f'}{r'}\right)[p] + \frac{1}{2}\mu(\alpha + \alpha')[k^2]$$

$$+ \mu[\alpha](k^2 + k'^2) = 0. \qquad (53\text{-}3)$$

(**b**) We will now transform the sum of the last two terms. We have first

$$(\alpha + \alpha')[k^2] = (\alpha + \alpha')(k'^2 - k^2)$$

$$= k'^2\alpha' - k^2\alpha + k'^2\alpha - k^2\alpha'$$

or, according to (50-9),

$$(\alpha + \alpha')[k^2] = kk'\alpha - kk'\alpha' + k'^2\alpha - k^2\alpha'$$

$$= -kk'(\alpha' - \alpha) - (k^2\alpha' - k'^2\alpha).$$

But,

$$k^2\alpha' - k'^2\alpha = k^2(\alpha' - \alpha) - (k'^2 - k^2)\alpha$$

$$= -(k'^2 - k^2)\alpha' + k'^2(\alpha' - \alpha),$$

and we obtain

$$k^2\alpha' - k'^2\alpha = \tfrac{1}{2}\{[\alpha](k^2 + k'^2) - (\alpha + \alpha')[k^2]\}.$$

It follows that

$$(\alpha + \alpha')[k^2] = -kk'[\alpha] - \tfrac{1}{2}[\alpha](k^2 + k'^2)$$

$$+ \tfrac{1}{2}(\alpha + \alpha')[k^2],$$

that is,

$$\tfrac{1}{2}(\alpha + \alpha')[k^2] = -\tfrac{1}{2}[\alpha](k^2 + k'^2) - [\alpha]kk'.$$

Thus,

$$\tfrac{1}{2}(\alpha + \alpha')[k^2] + [\alpha](k^2 + k'^2) = \tfrac{1}{2}[\alpha](k^2 + k'^2 - 2kk')$$
$$= \tfrac{1}{2}[\alpha](k' - k)^2 .$$

The relation (53-3) can be written

$$c^4[f^2] - c^2\left(\frac{f}{r} + \frac{f'}{r'}\right)[p] + \frac{1}{2}\mu c^2\left[\frac{f}{r}\right](k' - k)^2 = 0 ,$$

that is, according to (52-7),

$$c^2[f^2] - \left(\frac{f}{r} + \frac{f'}{r'}\right)[p] + \left[\frac{f}{r}\right]\frac{1}{2}\mu\frac{|[U]|^2}{|H|} = 0 . \qquad (53\text{-}4)$$

The equation (53-4) can be considered as the *relativistic Hugoniot equation.*

54. Classical Approximation of the Relativistic Magnetohydrodynamics

Now, we will try to deduce by approximation the shock equations of classical magnetohydrodynamics from the corresponding equations of the relativistic magnetohydrodynamics. While the classical theory permits the existence of the so-called creator shocks (or destructor shocks), the Theorem of §51(c) shows the nonexistence of such shocks in the relativistic frame. We will see the source of this disagreement.

(a) We consider only nontangential shocks and we let

$$u^\alpha n_\alpha = \frac{v}{c} , \qquad j = rv .$$

Thus,

$$a = \frac{j}{c} .$$

We seek the main parts of the shock equations (50-1), ..., (50-4), with respect to c^{-2}. We have first

$$[j] = [rv] = 0. \tag{54-1}$$

The invariance of $b = f\eta$ gives the equation

$$\left(1 + \frac{i'}{c^2}\right)\eta' = \left(1 + \frac{i}{c^2}\right)\eta.$$

It follows that

$$\eta' = \left(1 + \frac{i - i'}{c^2}\right)\eta \tag{54-2}$$

up to terms in c^{-4}. Thus, for the classical approximation, we have

$$[\eta] = 0. \tag{54-3}$$

The invariance of l gives

$$\left[\frac{f}{r} + \frac{1}{j^2}\left(p + \frac{1}{2}\mu|h|^2\right)\right] = 0.$$

Multiplying by $j^2 = r^2 v^2$, we obtain for the classical approximation

$$[rv^2 + p + \tfrac{1}{2}\mu|h|^2 = 0. \tag{54-4}$$

According to (54-2), the invariance of

$$H = \frac{c^2\eta^2}{j^2} - \frac{|h|^2}{r^2}$$

gives the relation

$$\frac{c^2}{j^2}\left(1 + 2\frac{i - i'}{c^2}\right)\eta^2 - \frac{|h'|^2}{r'^2} = \frac{c^2\eta^2}{j^2} - \frac{|h|^2}{r^2}.$$

It follows that

$$\left[2i\frac{\eta^2}{j^2} + \frac{|h|^2}{r^2}\right] = 0\,,$$

and, according to the previous relations,

$$\left[i + \frac{1}{2}\frac{|h|^2}{\eta^2}\,v^2\right] = 0\,. \tag{54-5}$$

The equation (54-5) can be also written

$$\left[i + \frac{1}{2}\,\frac{|t|^2 + \eta^2}{\eta^2}\,v^2\right] = 0,$$

that is,

$$\left[i + \frac{1}{2}\,v^2 + \frac{1}{2}\,\frac{|t|^2}{\eta^2}\,v^2\right] = 0\,. \tag{54-6}$$

We consider now the invariance of L. First of all,

$$c^{-2}\alpha = \frac{1}{r}\left(1 + \frac{i}{c^2}\right) - \mu\left(\frac{\eta^2}{j^2} - \frac{|h|^2}{c^2\,r^2}\right)$$

is equivalent to

$$\frac{1}{r} - \mu\,\frac{\eta^2}{j^2} \tag{54-7}$$

for the classical approximation. If (54-7) vanishes, Σ is a classical Alfven wave before the shock. Otherwise

$$k^2 = |t|^2 + \frac{j^2}{c^2}\,\frac{|h|^2}{r^2}$$

is equivalent to $|t|^2$, for the classical approximation. The invariance of L thus gives for this approximation

$$\left[|t|^2 \left(\frac{1}{r} - \mu \frac{\eta^2}{j^2}\right)^2\right] = 0. \tag{54-8}$$

The degeneration of k^2 *in* $|t|^2$ *explains the possibility of "creator and destructor shocks" in the classical theory.*

The equations (54-1), (54-3), (54-6), (54-8) are *the main equations of classical magnetohydrodynamics, written in a rest frame with respect to the shock.*

(**b**) Let us now seek the classical approximation of the relativistic Hugoniot equation (53-4). From (52-4), it follows that

$$U^\beta = \frac{c\eta}{j} t^\beta - \frac{|h|^2}{r^2} w^\beta$$

and we have, approximately,

$$[U^\beta] = \frac{c\eta}{j}[t^\beta]. \tag{54-9}$$

We obtain, therefore

$$\frac{|[U]|^2}{|H|} = \frac{c^2\eta^2/j^2}{c^2\eta^2/j^2}|[t]|^2 = |[t]|^2. \tag{54-10}$$

In the following part, we set

$$V = \frac{1}{r},$$

so that $i = \epsilon + pV$. The relation (52-4) can be written approximately

$$[i] - [p]\frac{V + V'}{2} + [V]\circ\frac{1}{4}\mu\,|[t]|^2 = 0.$$

An elementary calculation shows that

$$[pV] - [p]\frac{V + V'}{2} = \frac{p + p'}{2}[V],$$

and so we obtain

$$[\epsilon] + \frac{p + p'}{2}[V] + [V]\frac{1}{4}\mu\,|[t]|^2 = 0, \qquad (54\text{-}12)$$

which is the Hugoniot equation for the classical magnetohydrodynamics.

55. Thermodynamics of the Shocks

(a) Now, we consider p and S as main thermodynamical variables. From

$$c^2\,df = V dp + T dS,$$

it follows that

$$c^2 f'_p = V > 0, \qquad c^2 f'_S = T > 0. \qquad (55\text{-}1)$$

In the following part, we introduce systematically the function

$$\tau(p, S) = \frac{f}{r} = fV.$$

According to (55-1),

$$\frac{\partial}{\partial p}(c^2 f^2) = 2\tau. \qquad (55\text{-}2)$$

We consider V as a function of p and S. From

$$c^2\,d\tau = c^2 f\,dV + c^2 V df = c^2 f(V'_p dp + V'_S dS)$$

$$+ (V^2 dp + VTdS),$$

we deduce

$$\tau'_p = fV'_p + \frac{V^2}{c^2}, \qquad \tau'_S = fV'_S + \frac{VT}{c^2}.$$

It follows that

$$\tau''_{p^2} = fV''_{p^2} + 3\,\frac{VV'_p}{c^2}.$$

We are thus led to choose, for $\tau(p, S)$, the following *compressibility assumptions*

$$\tau'_p < 0, \qquad \tau'_S > 0, \qquad \tau''_{p^2} > 0. \tag{55-3}$$

For the classical approximation, these assumptions are reduced to

$$V'_p < 0, \qquad V'_S > 0, \qquad V''_{p^2} > 0,$$

that is, to the classical compressibility assumptions.

We will show (§ 58) that the inequality $\tau'_p < 0$ expresses that $v_0 < c$ and that the two other inequalities are satisfied by a relativistic polytropic gas.

(b) In the shock, we have necessarily at each point x of Σ:

$$S' \geq S. \tag{55-4}$$

We will prove the following theorem.

Theorem. Under the compressibility assumptions (55-3), we have the following inequalities

$$p' \geq p, \qquad f' \geq f, \qquad \tau' \leq \tau. \tag{55-5}$$

A shock wave is thus a compression wave and $V' \leq V$.

Let us suppose that, in $x \in \Sigma$, we have $p' < p$. From

(55-2), it follows that

$$c^2\{f^2(p, S) - f^2(p', S)\} = 2\int_{p'}^{p} \tau(p, S)\, dp\,.$$

We deduce, from the convexity condition $\tau''_{p^2} > 0$, that

$$c^2\{f^2(p, S) - f^2(p', S)\} < (p - p') \times \{\tau(p, S) + \tau(p', S)\}\,.$$

But $f'_S > 0$ and, $\tau'_S > 0$. It follows that

$$c^2\{f^2(p, S) - f^2(p', S')\} < (p - p') \times \{\tau(p, S) + \tau(p', S')\},$$

that is,

$$c^2[f^2] - (\tau + \tau')[p] > 0\,.$$

From the Hugoniot equation (53-4), it follows that

$$[\tau] = \tau(p', S') - \tau(p, S) < 0\,,$$

which is contradictory to $p' < p$, $S' \geq S$, and (55-3).

We have thus proved that $p' \geq p$; therefore, according to (55-1), $f(p', S') \geq f(p, S)$, that is, $f' \geq f$. It is now easy to prove that $\tau' \leq \tau$. We have

$$c^2\{f^2(p', S') - f^2(p, S')\} = 2\int_{p}^{p'} \tau(p, S')\, dp.$$

It follows that

$$c^2\{f^2(p', S') - f^2(p, S')\} \geq 2[p]\,\tau(p', S')\,.$$

But $f'_S > 0$. Thus

$$c^2\{f^2(p', S') - f^2(p, S)\} \geq 2[p]\tau(p', S').$$

We obtain

$$c^2[f^2] - 2\tau'[p] \geq 0,$$

and from the Hugoniot equation, we deduce

$$[\tau]\left\{-[p] - \frac{1}{2}\mu\frac{\|[U]\|^2}{|H|}\right\} \geq 0,$$

that is, $[\tau] \leq 0$ and the theorem is proved.

We have thus $\alpha' \leq \alpha$. If $\alpha' = \alpha \neq 0$ the shock vanishes. If $\alpha' = \alpha = 0$, the shock is an Alfven shock. For a non-vanishing shock which is not an Alfven shock, we have

$$\alpha' < \alpha. \tag{55-6}$$

(**c**) We will prove now the following result.

Theorem. For a nonvanishing shock which is not an Alfven shock, we have under the compressibility assumptions (55-3):

$$S < S'. \tag{55-7}$$

Let us suppose that, at the point $x \in \Sigma$,

$$S = S'. \tag{55-8}$$

From (55-2), it follows that

$$c^2\{f^2(p', S) - f^2(p, S)\} = 2\int_p^{p'} \tau(p, S)dp.$$

We deduce from the convexity condition that

$$c^2\{f^2(p', S) - f^2(p, S)\} \leq [p]\{\tau(p, S) + \tau(p', S)\},$$

that is, according to (55-8),

$$c^2[f^2] - (\tau + \tau')[p] \leq 0.$$

The Hugoniot equation then gives

$$[\tau]\,\frac{\|[U]\|^2}{|H|} \geq 0 .$$

If $[\tau]$ is $\neq 0$, we have $[\tau] < 0$ and

$$\frac{\|[U]\|^2}{|H|} = \frac{1}{|H|}\left(\frac{\alpha}{\alpha'} - 1\right)^2 |H|\,k^2 = \left(\frac{\alpha}{\alpha'} - 1\right)^2 k^2 = 0 .$$

Thus (55-8) implies $[\alpha] = 0$, which contradicts our assumptions.

56. Shock Wave and Alfven Waves

(a) Let us consider a shock wave Σ which corresponds to a nontangential shock and *which is not an Alfven shock*. At $x \in \Sigma$, we introduce an infinitesimal perturbation of the state prior to the shock. We obtain thus an infinitesimal perturbation of the state after the shock. These two perturbations are connected by the relations obtained by differentiation of the general shock equations. That is,

$$[\delta r u^\alpha + r\delta u^\alpha]\,n_\alpha = 0, \tag{56-1}$$

$$\left[\delta\eta\, u^\beta + \eta\,\delta u^\beta - \delta\left(\frac{a}{r}\right) h^\beta - \frac{a}{r}\,\delta h^\beta\right] = 0, \tag{56-2}$$

$$\left[\delta\left(\beta^2\,\frac{a}{r}\right) u^\beta + \beta^2\,\frac{a}{r}\,\delta u^\beta - \frac{1}{\mu}\,\delta q n^\beta - \delta\eta\, h^\beta - \eta\,\delta\, h^\beta\right] = 0. \tag{56-3}$$

We introduce at x an orthonormalized frame $\{e_{(\alpha)}\}$ such that $e_{(1)} = n$ and that $e_{(3)}$ is orthogonal to the 2-plane Π_x of § 52. In this frame

$$u^3 = 0, \qquad h^3 = 0 .$$

Let us consider the equations obtained for $\beta = 3$ in (56-2),

(56-3). We see thus that the system (56-1), (56-2), (56-3) is divided into two systems, the first of which includes only the perturbations δu^3 and δh^3, with

$$\left[\eta\,\delta u^3 - \frac{a}{r}\,\delta h^3\right] = 0, \tag{56-4}$$

$$\left[\beta^2\,\frac{a}{r}\,\delta u^3 - \eta\,\delta h^3\right] = 0. \tag{56-5}$$

The second system includes the other perturbations. In the following part, we consider the case *where* δu^3 *and* δh^3 *only are different from zero.* The thermodynamical variables being not perturbed, it follows that such perturbations correspond necessarily to infinitesimal Alfven shocks, that is, to Alfven waves.

(b) Let us consider, in the state prior to Σ, an Alfven wave of the kind A (§51). The vector A^α being invariant across the wave, such a wave gives at x a perturbation $(\delta u^3_A\,,\ \delta h^3_A)$ such that

$$\beta\,\delta u^3_A + \delta h^3_A = 0. \tag{56-6}$$

An Alfven wave of the kind B gives at x a perturbation $(\delta u^3_B\,,\ \delta h^3_B)$ such that

$$\beta\,\delta u^3_B - \delta h^3_B = 0. \tag{56-7}$$

The addition, at x, of an A-wave and of a B-wave gives an arbitrary perturbation $(\delta u^3, \delta h^3)$, with

$$\delta u^3 = \delta u^3_A + \delta u^3_B, \qquad \delta h^3 = \delta h^3_A + \delta h^3_B .$$

In order to obtain the perturbation $(\delta u^3, \delta h^3)$, it is sufficient to take

$$\begin{aligned} \delta h^3_A &= -\beta\,\delta u^3_A = \tfrac{1}{2}(\delta h^3 - \beta\,\delta u^3), \\ \delta h^3_B &= \beta\,\delta u^3_B = \tfrac{1}{2}(\delta h^3 + \beta\,\delta u^3). \end{aligned} \tag{56-8}$$

(**c**) The vectors A^α and B^α satisfy, at $x \in \Sigma$,

$$A^\alpha n_\alpha = \beta \frac{a}{r} + \eta , \qquad B^\alpha n_\alpha = \beta \frac{a}{r} - \eta .$$

It follows that

$$(A^\alpha n_\alpha)(B^\alpha n_\alpha) = \beta^2 \frac{a^2}{r^2} - \eta^2$$

$$= \frac{a^2}{\mu}\left(c^2 \frac{f}{r} + \mu \frac{|h|^2}{r^2} - \mu \frac{\eta^2}{a^2}\right),$$

that is,

$$(A^\alpha n_\alpha)(B^\alpha n_\alpha) = \frac{a^2}{\mu} \alpha . \qquad (56\text{-}9)$$

According to our conventions, we have $a < 0$. Let us suppose $b > 0$ and thus $\eta > 0$. It follows from the expression for $B^\alpha n_\alpha$ that the vector B^α has the same orientation as n^α with respect to Σ. The orientation of A^α is the orientation of B^α (or the contrary orientation) if α is > 0 (or < 0). If $b < 0$, the parts played by A^α and B^α would only be inverted.

57. Compatibility of a Shock Wave with the Alfven Waves

(**a**) Let us suppose that for the considered shock Σ we have

$$0 < \alpha' < \alpha . \qquad (57\text{-}1)$$

In the state before the shock Σ, the Alfven waves of the two kinds A and B which end at $x \in \Sigma$, give at this point an arbitrary perturbation $(\delta u^3, \delta h^3)$. From the relations (56-4) and (56-5), it follows that

$$\eta' \, \delta u'^3 - \frac{a}{r'} \, \delta h'^3 = \eta \, \delta u^3 - \frac{a}{r} \, \delta h^3 , \tag{57-2}$$

$$\beta'^2 \frac{a}{r'} \, \delta u'^3 - \eta' \, \delta h'^3 = \beta^2 \frac{a}{r} \, \delta u^3 - \eta \, \delta h^3 . \tag{57-3}$$

α' being $\neq 0$, this system in $(\delta u'^3, \delta h'^3)$ has one and only one solution which defines a perturbation of the state after the shock Σ ; this perturbation can go away from x along the corresponding Alfven waves A′ and B′. *There is compatibility between the shock wave and the Alfven waves.*

(b) Let us suppose now that we have

$$\alpha' < 0 < \alpha . \tag{57-4}$$

α being positive, the Alfven waves of the two kinds A and B still give, at $x \in \Sigma$, and arbitrary permutation $(\delta u^3, \delta h^3)$. But in the state after the shock, we have only an Alfven wave of the kind B′, which goes away from x and which gives a perturbation satisfying $\beta' \, \delta u'^3_B - \delta h'^3_B = 0$. From (57-2) and (57-3), it follows that

$$\eta \, \delta u^3 - \frac{a}{r} \delta h^3 = -\left(\beta' \frac{a}{r} - \eta'\right) \delta u'^3_B , \tag{57-5}$$

$$\beta^2 \frac{a}{r} \delta u^3 - \eta \, \delta h^3 = \beta' \left(\beta' \frac{a}{r} - \eta'\right) \delta u'^3_B . \tag{57-6}$$

If $(\delta u^3, \delta h^3)$ does not satisfy the relation

$$\left(\beta^2 \frac{a}{r} + \beta' \eta\right) \delta u^3 - \left(\beta' \frac{a}{r} + \eta\right) \delta h^3 = 0 , \tag{57-7}$$

we obtain, after the shock, a perturbation which does not correspond to a wave of the kind B′. Under our assumptions, the relation (57-7) is not an identity in $(\delta u^3, \delta h^3)$. If it were so, we should have

$$\beta = \beta' , \qquad \beta \frac{a}{r} + \eta = 0 ,$$

and α would be null.

Thus, there is no possible solution for the flow after the shock Σ. *There is no compatibility between the shock wave and the Alfven waves.*

(**c**) Let us suppose, finally, that we have

$$\alpha' < \alpha < 0 . \tag{57-8}$$

Before the shock, an Alfven wave of the kind B can end only at $x \in \Sigma$; it gives a perturbation $(\delta u^3_B , \delta h^3_B)$ satisfying

$$\beta \, \delta u^3_B - \delta h^3_B = 0 .$$

But there can go away from x an Alfven wave of the kind A before the shock Σ together with an Alfven wave of the kind B′ after the shock Σ, which corresponds, before the shock, to a perturbation $(\delta u^3 , \delta h^3)$ satisfying (57-7). We let

$$\delta u^3_B = \delta u^3 + \bar{\delta} u^3_A , \qquad \delta h^3_B = \delta h^3 + \bar{\delta} h^3_A ,$$

with

$$\delta h^3 = \theta \, \delta u^3 , \qquad \delta h^3_A = -\beta \, \delta u^3_A ,$$

where, according to (57-7),

$$\theta = \frac{\beta^2 \frac{a}{r} + \beta' \eta}{\beta' \frac{a}{r} + \eta} , \qquad \text{for } \beta' \frac{a}{r} + \eta \neq 0 .$$

From the equations

$$\beta \delta u^3 + \beta \bar{\delta} u^3_A = \beta \delta u^3_B ,$$

$$\theta\,\delta u^3 - \beta\,\overline{\delta} u^3_A = \beta\,\delta u^3_B,$$

we deduce

$$\delta u^3 = \frac{2\beta}{\theta+\beta}\,\delta u^3_B, \qquad \overline{\delta} u^3_A = \frac{\theta-\beta}{\theta+\beta}\,\delta u^3_B,$$

where

$$\theta + \beta = \frac{\beta + \beta'}{\beta'\dfrac{a}{r} + \eta}\left(\beta\frac{a}{r} + \eta\right)$$

is certainly different from zero. If $\beta'(a/r) + \eta = 0$, we obtain one and only one solution.

The perturbation $(\delta u^3_B, \delta h^3_B)$ being given, we have obtained the perturbation $(\overline{\delta} u^3_A, \overline{\delta} h^3_A)$ corresponding to the Alfven wave of the kind A which goes away from x before the shock, and the perturbation $(\delta u^3, \delta h^3)$ which gives a perturbation going away from x after the shock Σ along an Alfven wave of the kind B'. *There is still compatibility of the shock wave Σ with the Alfven waves.* We have the following result.

Theorem. A nontangential shock which is not an Alfven shock is compatible with the Alfven waves if and only if $\alpha\alpha'$ is positive.

(d) We call a *slow shock,* a shock such that

$$\alpha' < \alpha < 0,$$

and *a fast shock,* a shock such that

$$0 < \alpha' < \alpha.$$

Let us consider the main relation

$$k'^2\,\alpha'^2 = k^2\,\alpha^2.$$

For a slow shock $\alpha'^2 > \alpha^2$, therefore, $k'^2 < k^2$ and thus $|h'|^2 < |h|^2$. For a fast shock, the previous inequalities are reversed. We have, therefore, the following theorem.

Theorem. In a slow shock, the magnitude of the magnetic field decreases; in a fast shock it increases.

58. The Compressibility Conditions

We have proved the main theorem of the thermodynamics of shocks under the compressibility conditions (55-3). We now analyze these conditions.

(a) We know that, for a relativistic fluid with the state equation $r = r(f, S)$, the sound velocity v_0 is given by the relation

$$\frac{v_0^2}{c^2} = \frac{1}{\gamma}, \tag{58-1}$$

where

$$\gamma = \frac{f r'_f}{r}. \tag{58-2}$$

From $\tau = f/r$, we deduce by differentiation that

$$d\tau = \frac{1}{r}\,df - \frac{f}{r^2}\,(r'_f\,df + r'_S\,dS)$$

$$= V(1 - \gamma)\,df - V^2 f r'_S\,dS.$$

According to the expression for $c^2\,df$, we have

$$d\tau = \frac{V}{c^2}\,(1 - \gamma)(Vdp + TdS) - V^2 f r'_S\,dS.$$

It follows that the function $\tau = \tau(p, S)$ is such that

$$\tau'_p = \frac{V^2}{c^2}\,(1 - \gamma). \tag{58-3}$$

Thus *the inequality* $\tau'_p < 0$ *is equivalent to* $\gamma > 1$, *that is, to* $v_0 < c$.

(b) Let us now suppose that our relativistic fluid is a *polytropic gas* satisfying

$$pV = \frac{p}{r} = (c_p - c_v)T,$$

where c_v, c_p, $(c_p > c_v)$ are positive constants defining the specific heats. We have thus

$$x = \frac{c_p}{c_v} > 1. \tag{58-4}$$

The internal energy of the fluid is given by

$$\epsilon = c_v T = \frac{c_v}{c_p - c_v} pV = \frac{1}{x - 1} pV,$$

and the specific enthalpy by the relation

$$i = c_p T = \epsilon + pV = \frac{x}{x - 1} pV.$$

It follows that the index of the fluid is

$$f = 1 + \frac{x}{c^2(x - 1)} pV. \tag{58-5}$$

For the specific entropy, we have

$$S = c_p \log\left(p^{1/x} V\right),$$

so that

$$V = p^{-1/x} \exp(S/c_p). \tag{58-6}$$

The variable $\tau = fV$ is thus given by

$$\tau = V\left(1 + \frac{x}{c^2(x-1)}\, pV\right), \tag{58-7}$$

where V is given by (58-6) in terms of p and S. We consider p and S as the main thermodynamical variables. It is then easy, for $\tau(p, S)$, to calculate τ'_S. We have

$$\tau'_S = V'_S\left(1 + \frac{2x}{c^2(x-1)}\, pV\right),$$

where

$$V'_S = \frac{1}{c_p}\, p^{-1/x} \exp(S/c_p) = \frac{V}{c_p}\,.$$

We thus obtain

$$\tau'_S = \frac{V}{c_p}\left(1 + \frac{2x}{c^2(x-1)}\, pV\right), \tag{58-8}$$

and τ'_S is positive, according to (55-3).

(c) We consider now τ'_p and τ''_{p^2}. We have

$$\tau'_p = V'_p\left(1 + \frac{2x}{c^2(x-1)}\; pV\right) + \frac{x}{c^2(x-1)}\, V^2$$

but, according to (58-6),

$$V'_p = -\frac{1}{x}\, p^{-1/x-1} \exp(S/c_p) = -\frac{1}{x}\, p^{-1} V\,.$$

We thus obtain

$$\tau'_p = -V\left(\frac{1}{x}\, p^{-1} - \frac{x-2}{c^2(x-1)}\, V\right). \tag{58-9}$$

If the inequality $\tau'_p < 0$ is satisfied, we have

$$\frac{x-2}{c^2(x-1)} < \frac{1}{x} p^{-1}. \tag{58-10}$$

For τ''_{p^2}, we have

$$\tau''_{p^2} = -V'_p \left(\frac{1}{x} p^{-1} - \frac{2(x-2)}{c^2(x-1)} V\right) + V\frac{1}{x} p^{-2}$$

and, according to the value of V'_p,

$$\tau''_{p^2} = \frac{1}{x} p^{-1} V \left(\frac{1}{x} p^{-1} + p^{-1} - \frac{2(x-2)}{c^2(x-1)} V\right). \tag{58-11}$$

x being > 1, we have, according to the inequality (58-10),

$$\frac{(x-2)}{c^2(x-1)} V < \frac{1}{x} p^{-1} < p^{-1},$$

and thus

$$\frac{2(x-2)}{c^2(x-1)} V < \frac{1}{x} p^{-1} + p^{-1}.$$

From (58-11), there follows then the inequality $\tau''_{p^2} > 0$.

We obtain the following theorem.

Theorem. 1° *A relativistic fluid such that* $v_0 < c$ *satisfies the compressibility inequality*

$$\tau'_p < 0.$$

2° *If this fluid is a polytropic gas, the inequalities*

$$\tau'_S > 0, \qquad \tau''_{p^2} > 0$$

are satisfied.

We remark that for a polytropic gas

$$f = 1 + \frac{c_p}{c^2} T .$$

During the shock, f increases and, therefore, *so does the temperature* T.

CONCLUSION

In this book, we have traveled step-by-step through the relativistic treatment of hydrodynamics and magnetohydrodynamics. Our emphasis has been on the mathematical formulation of the basic equations of each theory, and their reduction to a form suitable for the application of the Leray theorem to the existence and uniqueness of solutions of the Cauchy problem.

In Chapter 1 we introduced the basic mathematical tools required throughout the remainder of the book and we gave applications to the exterior case and to the case of pure matter. In Chapter 2 we discussed the hydrodynamics and thermodynamics of a perfect fluid defined by an isotropic pressure, a density, and an equation of state. We discussed the characteristic surfaces of the resulting system of equations, and the existence and uniqueness of solutions of the Cauchy problem for such systems. Chapter 3 began with the relativistic formulation of electrodynamics. This led, in Chapter 3, to the system of equations describing a charged perfect fluid with vanishing conductivity. We proved the existence and uniqueness theorems for the Cauchy problem in this case. In Chapter 4, we introduced induction into the electromagnetic field. We then formulated the equations describing a perfect fluid with induction and with infinite conductivity magnetohydrodynamics. We proved the existence and uniqueness theorem for the Cauchy problem for such a system. And finally, in Chapter 5, we considered the two types of waves—Alfven and hydrodynamical waves. Shock waves, too, were found to be of two types—Alfven and hydrodynamical shocks—in analogy with the wave solutions of Chapter 4. We gave the relativistic form of the compressibility conditions for a fluid and we studied completely the thermodynamics of the shocks.

REFERENCES

1. Y. Choquet-Bruhat, "Théorèmes d'existence en mécanique des fluides relativistes," *Bull. Soc. Math. France*, **86**, 155–175 (1958).
2. Y. Choquet-Bruhat, "Fluides relativistes de conductivité infinie," *Astron. Acta*, **6**, 354–365 (1960).
3. L. Gärding, "Cauchy's problem for hyperbolic equations," *Lecture Notes*, University of Chicago (1957).
4. M. Gevrey, "Sur la nature analytique des solutions des équations aux dérivées partielles," *Ann. Ec. Norm. Sup.*, **35**, 129–189 (1917).
5. J. Leray, "Hyperbolic differential equations," *Lecture Notes*, Institute for Advanced Study, Princeton (1953).
6. J. Leray and Y. Ohya, *Systèmes Linéaires Hyperboliques Nonstricts*, Conférences au Collège de France, mimeographed (1965).
7. A Lichnerowicz, *Théories Relativistes de la Gravitatior et de l'Électromagnétisme*, Masson, Paris (1955).
8. A. Lichnerowicz, "Théorèmes d'existence et d'unicité par un fluide thermodynamique relativiste," *C.R. Acad. Sc. Paris*, **260**, 3291–3295 (1965); "Etude mathématique des équations de la magnétohydrodynamique relativiste," *C.R. Acad. Sc.* Paris, **260**, 4449–4453, (1965).
9. A. Lichnerowicz, "Etude mathématique des fluides thermodynamiques relativistes," *Comm. Math. Phys.*, **1**, 328–373 (1966).

10. C. Möller, *The Theory of Relativity*, Clarendon Press, Oxford (1952).
11. Y. Ohya, "Le problème de Cauchy pour les équations à caractéristiques multiples," *J. Math. Soc. Japan*, **16**, 268–286 (1964).
12. Pham-Mau-Quan, "Inductions électromagnétiques en relativité générale," *Arch. Rat. Mech. Anal.*, **1**, 54–79 (1957).
13. Pham-Mau-Quan, "Magnétohydrodynamique relativiste," *Ann. Inst. Henri Poincaré*, nouv. série, **2**, 151–165 (1965).
14. A. H. Taub, Phys. Rev., **74**, 328–334 (1948); "On circulation in relativistic hydrodynamics," *Arch. Rat. Mech. Anal.*, **3**, 312–324 (1959).
15. E. Anderson, *Magnetohydrodynamic Shock Waves*, Mass. Inst. of Techn. Press, Cambridge (1963).
16. H. Cabannes, *Magnétodynamique des Fluides*, C.D.U., Paris (1965).
17. F. Hoffmann and E. Teller, "Magnetohydrodynamic shocks," *Phys. Rev.*, **80**, 692–703 (1950).
18. A. Lichnerowicz, "Sur les ondes de choc en magnétohydrodynamique relativiste," *C.R. Acad. Sc. Paris*, **262**, 153–154 (1966).
19. R. Polovin, "Shock waves in magnetohydrodynamics," *Sov. Phys. Usp.*, **3**, 677–688 (1961).
20. P. Reichel, *Basic Notions of Relativistic Hydromagnetics*, A.E.C. Research Report, New York University (1958).

INDEX